T

d.

Happy reading

Best wishes

Mahud Ervin

07/07/2019

MANTO

ON AND ABOUT

MANTO

18 ENGLISH TRANSLATIONS
OF SELECTED WORKS
OF MANTO AND HIS FRIENDS

Translated By
MUJAHID ESHAI

SANG-E-MEEL PUBLICATIONS
25, SHAHRAH-E-PAKISTAN (LOWER MALL) LAHORE.

891.4393   Eshai, Mujahid
            Manto on and about Manto/ tr. by
        Mujahid Eshai.-Lahore: Sang-e-Meel
        Publications, 2014.
            245pp.
            1. Literature - Manto.   I. Title.

2014
Published by:
Afzaal Ahmad
Sang-e-Meel Publications,
Lahore.

ISBN-10: 969-35-2797-6
ISBN-13: 978-969-35-2797-1

Sang-e-Meel Publications
25 Shahrah-e-Pakistan (Lower Mall), Lahore-54000 PAKISTAN
Phones: 92-423-722-0100 / 92-423-722-8143 Fax: 92-423-724-5101
http://www.sang-e-meel.com e-mail: smp@sang-e-meel.com
PRINTED AT: HAJI HANIF & SONS PRINTERS, LAHORE.

Dedicated to the memory of my parents and
to the love and affection of my wife and
daughters

CONTENTS

A FEW WORDS

MUJAHID ESHAI

Life is a theme with innumerable variations. Some of these variations may annoy us, depress and sadden or simply not agree with us while others provide enjoyment, cause for laughter, perhaps food for thought and at times a reminder of the grim realities of and about our existence. Each variation has a reason behind it, individual or societal. Since the individual is part of the society therefore the ills in our society need to be looked at without the proverbial rose-tinted glasses in order to improve the lot of humanity at large not just a select part of it.

It is a fact that humans cannot experience each and every aspect of life in detail. Their personal knowledge and experience is enhanced by interaction with others, works of an artiste, stories, tales, opinions, thoughts, poetry, prose, paintings and sculpture. The way in which the innumerable facets of life and thought are presented before us should depict bare reality. Of course, there will be those images which are creation of a fantasy, of a dream world and riches beyond imagination of the ordinary mortal. But that is, for most, far fetched and not reality. Life is too precious to be wasted in a world of wishes and desires although these are necessary to keep one going forward. Life is harsh and a peaceful existence even harder. Success, howsoever, one may decide to define it, is sought by all. Whether we succeed or not is another reality that would have to be lived with.

Saadat Hassan Manto succeeded in creating stories. Stories that on the surface appear to be full of ambiguities, provocations, sarcasm, taunts and jibes but are actually harsh statements on the stark uncertainty and realities of life, the failures of humans who may have thought of themselves as indefatigable, man's inhumanity to man and the gross darkness that envelops the lives of so many.

Saadat Hassan Manto saw and felt the endless exploitation of man by man. He too suffered at its hands when publishers and film makers did not pay him either for his superb outpourings or according to his stature. And when he spoke through his pen portraying exploitation of the many by the few, the contradictions in our society, the economic deprivation of a vast number, the so-called guardians of the society raised a hue and cry against it as if the world being presented before them did not exist or should not be seen to exist. This was and is even today quite simply hypocrisy.

One could go on and on about these matters but the question that one needed an answer to was: What made Manto the man that we saw through his writings? One does not profess to be either a psychologist or a literary critic but as an ordinary reader of his writings seeks to understand the writer, why he wrote and what he wrote. There could be no better place than Manto's own writings through which various nuances of his character, as reflected in his ironic and satirical writings, became evident and made it easier to understand his life and works.

The objective as stated above, may have been a personal desire of an avid reader of Manto, but why share it with everybody? One reckons that there is a need to do so in order to make our younger generations understand the real side of life as so artistically written by Manto. There is also an urgent requirement to present the modern day classicists of Urdu language belonging to this country in a language that the youngsters understand. To talk of those who existed a hundred or more years ago is something the modern youth does not relate to readily. Those who wrote after the partition of the Sub-Continent, notwithstanding the fact that they were established writers before that, now wrote about the woes, the ills, the hopes and aspirations of a new nation. Whilst the old classicist should not be forgotten, the modern day writer is suddenly more acceptable to those who belong to this country because the reader can relate to him/her as one of their own. They by reading these works can understand that the writer is now talking about their society and the immediate environment that they live in and not an era that one would have to discover in order to appreciate.

Most short stories may be considered figments of a writer's imagination. But then there are stories that are based on reality and facts as they exist. Such stories may be harsh in terms of the reality that they are depicting, they may appear to be crass, crude and vulgar but then who can deny that a lot of what exists around us is exactly that. Life is not as glamorous as it may be made out by some. For the majority it is an endless story of one problem after the other, whether social, economic, psychological or sexual. In fact the psychological make up of a person is most often than not defined by the immediate environs and the resulting problems that emerge from his/her interaction with society. The good times, the glamour, the glitz, the jet-setting and the partying with a lot of hoopla is perhaps the escape that most want from the problems that confront us. To understand and tackle reality is difficult and may at times lead to indulging in such actions or engaging in such work that may be frowned upon by the society at large. The question therefore arises what should these people do? They do what they can, regardless of its morality, to eke out an existence, and stopping short of committing suicide. The society has to be made aware of these real problems because it is a societal responsibility to create the environment where all can have access to the means that make life more acceptable and amenable to the society at large. This awareness can only be created if the issues are talked of plainly, bluntly and in a manner that people can understand. Anything that is covered in gloss or superb rhetoric cannot represent the seamier and harsh side of life which is to be corrected, a responsibility of the society. The gloss can titillate, overawe one by its opulence, immensity and ostentatiousness but cannot lead to or create the desire for the correction of societal ills and depravity.

So, was Manto a social reformer who took up the cudgels to write about the dark and depraved goings on in the society? I do not think so because Manto never took sides for one cause or the other. He simply narrated the facts as he saw them before his readers and allowed them to make up their minds. His neutrality in all matters whilst drawing attention to the issues is remarkable. His use of words, though simple, is framed in emphatic fashion to bring out the essence of the situation and creating a feeling in the reader to get up and do something about it. The purpose expressed or otherwise, never had been to titillate the reader by indulging in lurid description of sexuality or profanity. This principle was always adhered to by him. The aim, it appears, was always to make the reader ponder about the inhumane situations, the meanness and nastiness of man and the socio-political and economic disparities that drove individuals to commit indecent acts.

Manto did not write short stories only. His non-fictional writings and dramas are also part of his repertoire whilst the work done for the film industry in Bombay (now Mumbai) is not available. The political satire in his epic letters to Uncle Sam is as relevant today as at the time they were written. Without getting into the literary merits of the letters written to Pandit Jawaharlal Nehru, a reading of the same gives the reader an idea of the outstanding issues that required settlement, some of which even today remain a bone of contention between the two countries.

Partition of the sub-continent was an issue that Manto did not reconcile with. Whilst he did migrate from Bombay to Lahore he was not at home. He could not really reconcile with the reasons why partition had to take place. He could not understand the carnage and bloodshed and man's inhumanity towards man. This state is reflected in most of his stories penned after Partition.

Manto was prosecuted six times on charges of obscenity but exonerated each time though on a couple of occasions he was penalized and made to pay a fine. Three of these cases were before partition whilst the remaining in Pakistan. The details of three of these cases were penned by Manto himself in his inimitable style and have been translated for the readers. The writing of the short story "THANDA GOSHT" was a result of the conflicts in Manto's mind about partition and the barbarous occurrences during the course of it. His prosecution because of this writing was carried out and heard by people who more than anything else had wanted to prove themselves holier than the Pope. However, the attempts to proscribe him ended in failure but forced Manto to say:

"You the reader know me as a story writer and the courts of this country know me as a pornographer. The government sometimes calls me a communist, at other times a great writer. Most of the time, I am denied all means of livelihood, only to be offered opportunities of gainful work on other occasions. I have been called an expendable appendage to society and accordingly expelled. And sometimes I am told that my name has been placed on the state-approved list. As in the past, so today, I have tried to understand what I am. I want to know what my place in this country that is called the largest Islamic state in the world is. What use am I here? You may call it my imagination, but the bitter truth is that so far I have failed to find a place for myself in this country called Pakistan which I greatly love. That is why I am always restless. That's why sometimes I am to be found in a lunatic asylum, other times in a hospital. I have yet to find a niche in Pakistan." (Translation by (Late) Khalid Hassan).

The seven years that Manto spent in the newly founded state till his death were turbulent years. The partition entailing the transmigration of millions, the ensuing blood shed and carnage, the death of Quaid-e-Azam, the assassination of Mr. Liaquat Ali Khan and the rehabilitation of refugees in a land where everything except human carcasses was in scarcity was more than enough to cause the kind of catalytic intellectual upheaval that a sensitive person like Manto displayed in his post-1947 writings. His efforts, both fiction and non-fiction, reflected this immense tragedy and the suffering in such situations of all regardless of creed or caste. Manto maintained a neutral posture and did not take sides. He presented the human tragedies to his reader as he perceived them and allowed them to decide the morality and ethics of the events and the characters as they were unfolded before them. Manto's approach of presenting situations and dialogues in the language used by the characters in real life landed him in trouble as those who deemed themselves to be the guardians of Society's morality did not accept the language used as permissible amongst perhaps the elitist class. However, one does not think that there was a class struggle that Manto was indulging in through his writings but a mere presentation of the reality without any frills and laces. The majority understood him. The minority deemed it vulgar, profane and obscene. Manto suffered because of what the minority desired as it remained in control of peoples lives.

Manto never indulged in writing any graphic details of sexual acts. His use of metaphors and innuendos were sufficient to draw the attention of the reader to such matters but never beyond that. He did not have to as he was not seeking to be a quick commercial success but a writer of the grief, sorry, filth, grime, squalor and inhumanity that the majority were passing their lives in. It is that which he wanted redressed. But he was punished for saying so.

Manto's outlook towards life may have also been affected to an extent and no more because of an austere father, a doting mother who was not accepted by the family, being the second wife, half-brothers being educated abroad, illness, weakening eye sight and a prolonged incomplete formal education. Despite this one notices vitality, a fun loving nature and an almost elfin and naughty spirit in Manto as reflected in his non-fictional, personal narratives. The short story side, however, remains somber.

The selection of Manto's non-fictional writings, translated and included in this collection, bring out some of these facets quite clearly. Three writings on Manto by two of his friends, Krishan Chander and Ahmed Nadeem Qasmi, and one by his mentor, Bari Alig, have also been included to bring out Manto's relationship, professional and personal, with those around him. These views are supplemented by Manto's profile of Ismat Chughtai, a part of this anthology. All these reflect a sad, excitable, restless, emotional, impulsive, forgiving, down to earth, loving, impish Manto. Perhaps he was all of these but most importantly he was one of the leading short story writers of the Indian Sub-continent in the twentieth century who was subjected to great torment and abuse by the guardians of the society.

I trust that the readers shall find this anthology of a very few of the Manto non-fictional writings to their liking. I have tried to remain as true to the written Urdu text as printed in the series of writings about and by Manto.

I must also thank my younger daughter, Kanwal Eshai and her husband Sameer Ahmad for taking the pains to assist me in correcting the original translations. If there still remain any errors, these may be attributed only to me and I accept full responsibility for the same.

Happy reading!

LAHORE, March, 2014

SHADOWS ACROSS
THE RADIANT MOON

Abandoning Bombay, transiting through Karachi, I arrived in Lahore on 7th or 8th January, 1948. For three months my thoughts were in a strange turmoil. I could not make out my exact location. Was I in Bombay or Karachi, or at my friend Hassan Abbas's house, or Lahore where innumerable restaurants were engaged in organizing song and dance parties for the purpose of collecting money for the Quaid-e-Azam Fund.

For three months I remained in a state of utter bewilderment. I felt as if there were numerous reels of various films running simultaneously on my mind's screen and all of them were overlapping each other— crowded and busy markets and lanes of Bombay, the small but fast moving trams and donkey carts of Karachi and sometimes the raucous restaurants of Lahore. I could not make out where I was – I just sat in a chair, lost in thought.

Finally, one day I was jolted out of this state of limbo, as the money I had brought with me from Bombay had nearly run out, used partially at home and partially at the Clifton Bar, away from home. I now became aware of the fact that I was in Lahore, whereto I used to travel occasionally in connection with my law suits and wherefrom I used to buy lots of beautiful sandals at the Karnal Shop.

I now started worrying about the type of work that one could engage in. On seeking information, I was informed that the Partition had crippled the film industry. Activities of Film Companies as displayed on the advertisement billboards were limited to these hoardings – I felt anguished – allotment of property was the rage. Refugees and non-Refugees, alike, using their influence and connections, were totally engaged in getting factories and shops allotted. I was advised to partake in this activity but I did not join this loot and plunder.

During the course of days I learnt that Faiz Ahmed Faiz and Chiragh Hassan Hasrat were planning to bring out a daily, laid out in the modern style. I met these gentlemen. The name of the newspaper was "IMROOZE" which today is on every ones lips. On my first meeting, a dummy of the newspaper was being prepared. When I met them a second time, probably four issues had already been published. The presentation of the paper delighted me. I felt a desire to write. But when I sat down to do so, I discovered that my thoughts were still in a total clutter.

Despite effort, I just could not disassociate Hindustan from Pakistan and Pakistan from Hindustan. Repeatedly questions causing further distress and confusion arose in my mind - is the literature of Pakistan going to be different? If so, then what kind shall it be? Who shall be the owner of all the literature that had been created in United Hindustan, - is it also to be partitioned? Are not the basic problems of Hindustanis and Pakistanis the same? Will Urdu cease to exist over there? What form shall Urdu take in Pakistan? Will our State be a religious State? We will always be loyal to the State but will we be permitted to criticize the Government? Will the conditions, after Independence, be any different from the era of the foreign rule?

All around me, wherever I looked, I could only see utter anarchy. Some people were very happy because they had suddenly acquired wealth. But there was a sense of insecurity in this state of happiness, as if the acquired wealth was going to be suddenly snatched away in the days to come. Most were depressed and worried as they had arrived after losing all their worldly possessions.

Look at the Refugee Camps. Here one sees anarchy in a state of total fright. Somebody says to me: conditions are now somewhat better, earlier they were execrable. I start to wonder that if this were a better state how bad must bad have been. A strange situation in which the instincts of intense anger that deprives humans of intellect and religious morality, prevail in an overwhelming as well as a totally devoid manner. The laughter of one overrides the wail of the other. The continued existence of one life was at odds with the state of near - death of the other. Two streams were flowing. One of life and the other of death, but between them is a barren strip on which despair and want, hunger and thirst move together. The air is full of gloom, like at the start of summer when the shrill of the aimlessly flying kites is full of sadness. Equally sad, indeed, also sound the occasional cheers of "Pakistan Zindabad" and "Quaid-e-Azam Zindabad."

The air waves of radio sounded tired and bored relaying day in and day out the ballads of the deceased Poet Iqbal. The feature programs broadcast are on topics such as: How to rear hens. How to make shoes? What is tanning? How many people arrived and left the Refugee Camps?

Nearly all trees are denuded. The poor refugees have ripped the tree barks off to provide warmth to their bodies. The branches have been lopped off to provide fodder for the stomach. These stark naked trees add to the prevailing air of woe and misery.

The buildings look cheerless and those who reside within appear in mourning. Outwardly the residents appear to laugh and play and if they find some work they do it. But all of this seemed to be happening in a void, a void which despite brimming with people was completely empty.

I met my friend Ahmed Nadeem Qasmi as well as Sahir Ludhianvi and a number of other people. Everyone's thinking, like my own, is paralyzed. I hope that some of the tremors of this massive earthquake that has hit us all are still, perhaps, stuck within the volcano. If these too were to erupt, perhaps, the atmosphere might lighten up, and we would only then find out the exact state of the prevailing situation.

I am fed up of thinking. So, I engage myself in loitering about. Aimless wanderings throughout the day. I stay silent and listen to what others say - pointless conversations, illogical discussions, very rudimentary and basic political arguments. One good though emerges from this meaningless odyssey. The clouds of confusion and chaos within my head start to subside slowly. I decide to write light veined articles. Thus essays like, "Types of Noses," "Post Scribing on Walls," were penned for "IMROOZE" and appreciated. Slowly but steadily the mood turned ironic resulting in articles like "When my eyes opened the Next Morning." I became conscious of the fact that my pen had finally established an opening through the fog surrounding the environs and I felt elated and unburdened as if a huge weight had lifted off my thoughts and mind. I started to write in earnest in this style. Later a collection of such writings was published in the form of a book entitled "Bitter, Sour and Sweet."

My mind was still not ready to pen short stories. I considered writing in this literary genre serious business. So, I kept resisting the urge to write a short story. But one day my dear friend Ahmed Nadeem Qasmi, who probably had also got tired of writing meaningless stuff, left Radio Pakistan, Peshawar, and came to Lahore. In collaboration with the "Institute for Promotion of Urdu" he had started the publication of a monthly magazine titled "NAQOOSH." Despite his repeated insistence I just could not get myself round to writing a short story for the first few issues. It was only when he was truly annoyed, that I wrote my first short story in Pakistan, "THANDA GOSHT," (COLD MEAT), which has now become the title of a collection of my short stories.

Qasmi Sahib started reading the short story in my presence. He kept reading it in utter silence. I could therefore not ascertain his reactions to it. After finishing the reading, he, in an apologetic tone, said to me: "Sorry Manto Sahib, the story is excellent but too hot for NAQOOSH."

I never argue with Qasmi Sahib. Very quietly I took the short story back and said to him: "Very well. I will now write another short story for you. Please, come back tomorrow evening."

When Qasmi Sahib returned the following evening, I was still busy writing the final lines of my second short story, "KHOL DO," (OPEN UP). I said to Qasmi Sahib: "Please be seated. I will just complete my short story in one minute and give it to you." Since the last lines of the story were very important Qasmi Sahib had to wait for a long time. Once completed, I gave the manuscript to him and said: "Please read. Hope to God you like it."

Qasmi Sahib started reading the short story. When he reached the last few lines, I observed as if something had thoroughly shaken him up. After completing the reading, he remained silent. I enquired: "How was it?" It was quite visible that he was touched by the story. He replied: "It's good. I am taking it with me." And he departed.

"KHOL DO" was published by Qasmi Sahib in the third edition of "NAQOOSH." The reading public liked it. Every one seemed to react in a similar manner. The last lines of the story appeared to have a moving effect on all. But suddenly a bombshell was dropped. The Government considered the effect of the short story as contrary to public harmony and ordered that the publication of NAQOOSH be banned for six months. The daily newspapers agitated and wrote copiously against this step but the order stayed put.

One day I jokingly said to Qasmi Sahib: "If you had published "THANDA GOSHT," perhaps, this lightning might not have struck your abode."

Several days later the Deputy Editor of "ADAB-E-LATEEF" came to me and took away from me the short story "THANDA GOSHT." The short story was transcribed, printing plates prepared, the first proofs produced, edited and returned to the Press, when someone read the copy. The Printing press immediately refused to print the text and the magazine appeared without this story. When Chaudhary Barkat Ali, Editor, who was in Quetta at the time, returned, he tried his utmost to have the story "THANDA GOSHT" published in the next issue of "ADAB-E- LATEEF" but without success. The manuscript was returned to me.

While all this was going on I received several letters from Ms. Shireen Mumtaz of "NAYA DAUR" in Karachi pleading that I send a short story for her magazine. I immediately mailed the manuscript of "THANDA GOSHT" to her. Quite a few days later I received a letter from her stating "we had prolonged deliberations on whether to publish it or not. The short story is very good. I like it a lot. But we are afraid that it may become a victim of Punjab Government's censorship." So the short story "THANDA GOSHT" is again returned to me, ice cold. I now thought that it should not be published in any magazine.

The six month ban on "NAQOOSH" was lifted just before its completion. I prepared a collection of stories for the new editorial board of the magazine, naming the collection "NAMROOD KI KHUDAI" (Godliness of Nimrod), and included both "KHOL DO" and "THANDA GOSHT" in it. But God had decided on a different fate.

My dear friend Arif Abdul Mateen had been appointed the editor of the magazine "JAVED". He pursued me endlessly to give him the "THANDA GOSHT" manuscript for publication. I dilly dallied for a long while but eventually succumbed to his pleadings. I wrote a note to the owner of "NAYA IDARA", Chaudhary Nazir Ahmed Sahib, stating that "those responsible for "JAVED" probably desire the confiscation of their magazine, so kindly pass on to them the manuscript of "THANDA GOSHT." Arif Sahib received the manuscript and published it in a special issue of "JAVED" in March 1949.

The magazine became available in the market as well as being circulated to all internal and external distribution agencies. So far so good. A month elapsed without any problems arising. I felt satisfied that no catastrophe was now going to befall on us because of the publication. But the Press Branch of the Government was still controlled by Chaudhry Mohammed Hussain (now deceased). Although he had become physically weak due to advanced age, he still retained sufficient power to yank hard and when he did so it launched the Press Department into frenzied action.

I heard rumors circulating that the police had seized copies of the special issue of "JAVED." I enquired from the few people I knew. Some contradicted the news whilst others termed it a publicity stunt of the "JAVED" publishing house. While this was going on I received a letter from Mr. Naseer Anwar, the owner of the magazine:

"Manto Sahib,

A bit of news for you – Today the police raided the offices of "JAVED." Whilst carrying out the search they seized a few remaining past issues of the magazine. Some others were inspected in detail but the Dispatch Register made it abundantly clear that all copies of the particular issue had been dispatched to various stations. They noted the addresses of all agencies from the register and ordered that no further prints of the particular issue should be supplied. This action is a prelude to formal arrests and I am certain that we shall soon be standing in the prisoners' dock. However, is it not strange that a local organization is referring to this raid as an imaginative piece of publicity? I wonder why?

Anyway, let it be so, the news will soon be automatically confirmed. I only want to say, be ready to go to the place where you were sentenced to thrice but then later exonerated. I think this will be the last time."

The news was soon confirmed. The matter was placed before the Press Advisory Board, whose convener was Colonel Faiz Ahmed Faiz, Editor daily "Pakistan Times." Mr. Naseer Anwar, the owner of "JAVED" was also present on the occasion. In his words, a brief summary of the proceedings: "The Press Advisory Board held its meeting in the offices of the daily 'Pakistan Times.' Faiz Ahmed Faiz was the convener. Other participants were F.W. Burton (Daily Civil and Military Gazette), Maulana Akhtar Ali (Daily Zamindar), Hamid Nizami (Daily Nawai Waqt), Waqar Ambalvi (Safeena) and Aminuddin Sehrai (Jadeed Nizam). Choudhry Mohammed Hussain presented the special issue of "JAVED." He recounted the rebellious and provocative articles and poems it contained the poems included "Slavery to Freedom," "Raqs-e-Bismil" and "Saylab-e-Cheen." Articles brought into discussion were "Lorraine to Faletti," "Khetta Bahadur ki Jai" and "How far is China." Faiz continuously rebutted the charges levied by the Government. The other members concurred with him and thus this particular politically motivated charge was done away with. But "THANDA GOSHT" bore the brunt of the wrath, particularly when Faiz declared that it was not obscene. Maulana Akhtar Ali roared "No. No. This kind of literature will not be tolerated in Pakistan."Mr Sehrai agreed and Waqar Sahib declared the article slanderous and execrable. Hamid Nizami toed the "Nawai Waqt" line. And when Chaudhry Sahib started explaining "THANDA GOSHT" to Mr. Burton, I with great difficulty controlled my laughter. He said: "The theme of the story is that we Muslims are so shameless that the Sikhs did not even hesitate to rape one of our dead girls." Amusing though it was, but when Chaudhry Sahib persisted with his incorrect interpretation of the story I was saddened. I tried my utmost to make him understand and Faiz Sahib also tried to satisfy him from all aspects but it was eventually decided that only the Honorable Court shall now decide the matter.

A few days later Naseer Anwar, Arif Abdul Mateen and I were arrested. The arresting sub-inspector was Choudhry Khuda Baksh, a thorough gentleman. He kept my house under surveillance for a number of days because I used to be out most of the time. Eventually one day he succeeded in meeting me and in a very civil manner requested me: "Tomorrow morning please come with a friend to the Civil Lines Police station so that your bail is done." Since I had dealt with a number of police personnel before, I was impressed with the very gentle approach of Choudhry Khuda Baksh.

The next morning I reported to the Police Station. My friend Sheikh Saleem signed off as surety and thus we were done with the first stage in the case.

Arif Abdul Mateen looked extremely distraught and his throat would go dry. This was odd because he was an active member of the Communist Party but yet so apprehensive of the Courts. Anyway the summons were issued and on the appointed date of the hearing, the three of us appeared at the District Courts.

For me this was not a new place. I had come here often in connection with my last three trials and thought of it as wasted time. Though the place was referred to as the Civil Courts it was extremely filthy. Mosquitoes, flies, insects of all kind, the clink clunk of the handcuffs and foot chains, the incongruous sound of ancient typewriters, three legged chairs with the cane seats non-existent and the plaster falling off the walls. The lawn devoid of grass just like the bald head of an unclean and dirty Kashmiri. Burqa clad women sat cross legged on the uncarpeted, dust covered floor. Some were spewing out dirty abuses while others simply sat pouting. Inside the court rooms the Magistrates were seated at hideous looking tables and hearing cases. Their friends were seated close by with whom pleasantries were exchanged even during the course of the trials. Words cannot describe the pathetic state of the Civil Courts – the air is totally different, the environment odd to say the least, the language strange and the innuendos peculiar- a very queer place indeed. May God keep everyone away from it.

If you desired a copy of a document you had to submit an application and attach "wheels" to it. If you wanted to examine a file, again "wheels" were necessary. If the work was required to be done expeditiously, extra "wheels" were required. It was not necessary to explore closely this state. Your eyes could easily observe that every application moved only on "wheels." From one office to the next, four wheels, from second to third office eight wheels and so forth. If you were not a habitual criminal, your heart may have prayed for someone to attach wheels to yourself, give a hefty push and roll you out of the District Courts.

I needed a lawyer to represent me in the trial. Before appearing in the Court, I had met one Mr. Tassaduq Hussain Khalid, who graciously volunteered to appear for me saying he would be delighted to do so. So, quite naturally he was asked to undertake the bother.

Khalid Sahib arrived and we presented ourselves in the court of Mian A.M.Saeed, P.C.S., Magistrate Class 1. Mian Sahib was once a Captain in the army but his gun had been taken away and instead the scales of justice thrust in his hands. Dark complexioned, small darting eyes and light weight, he sat in the chair with an air of assurance. We, the accused, after offering salutations, went and stood in the dock, but he without taking any notice of us turned towards Mr. Tassaduq Hussain. The bails were again executed where after a date for the second hearing was granted. We said our goodbyes to Mian Saeed Sahib and walked out of the Court room. It was the month of June and all our throats were parched, but Arif Abdul Mateen appeared to have a frog stuck in his throat. I wished that a Party member was around.

Another two to three hearings went by. The weather was extremely hot but we willy-nilly had to stand outside the court room until summoned. It was feared that if we moved away the Magistrate would take umbrage. From the very start his attitude had been rather severe. It seemed, as if in his heart he had already framed a decision against us. Mr. Khalid said to me "Should we not get the case transferred from this particular court. The Magistrate's attitude seems quite hostile." I replied that "there was no point in doing this as we do not see any different attitude in another court. Better leave it where it is."

Mr. Khalid agreed and proceeded to attend a further two or three hearings. The Prosecution presented Mr. Mohammed Yaqoob, son of Mian Ghulam Qadir, Manager Kapoor Art Press, Lahore, Sheikh Mohammed Tufail Haleem, Assistant Superintendent, Deputy Commissioner's office, Lahore, Syed Ziauddin Ahmed, translator Press Branch Punjab Government and some other persons as witnesses.

In Syed Ziauddin's opinion the entire story "THANDA GOSHT" was obscene. Replying to a question from Mr. Khalid he said "As far as the effort of the author is concerned it is honest, except for his style of expression and the usage of bad words." In response to another question by Mr. Khalid, whether in the witnesses' opinion the author ought not to use such words in the speech of a character which brought out emphatically a truer depiction of that character; Syed Sahib said that words to be used must be such that the personality of the character is established. He also accepted that "It was the task of a writer to create good and bad characters."

The Prosecution finally rested its case. The Magistrate, to formally comply with the laid down regulations, asked us a few questions which were answered briefly and to the point. This business is known as framing of the charge and goes somewhat like this:

Question by the Court: "You, as the author of a story entitled "THANDA GOSHT," which is obscene, are accused of sending the same for publication to Naseer Anwar, Printer and Publisher, co-accused along with Arif Abdul Mateen, Editor of the magazine "JAVED" in a special edition of the Magazine. This act is charged under Section 292 of the Penal Code. You are required to provide reasons why you should not be sentenced for the crime."

Response of Accused (by Mr. Khalid): "I did send the short story "THANDA GOSHT" to "JAVED" for publication but it is not obscene nor do I perceive it as obscene. I consider it to be reformist."

Question by the Court: "Why then has this case been lodged?"

Response of Accused: "The Police knows better, as their standards of morality and reform are different."

Question by the Court: "Do you want to say something more?"

Response of Accused: "Not at the present moment."

We were then asked to produce a list of witnesses for the defense. Since we had already prepared such a list it was presented forthwith. Mian Saeed Sahib on seeing thirty two names on the list was irritated and said: "I am not going to allow such a crowd to appear."   But Mr. Khalid insisted that each witness was extremely important in his own right. Mian Saeed behaved in a sarcastic manner when on reading the name of Ms. Mumtaz Shireen enquired as to who this Mumtaz Shanti was. Various people in the court laughed at Mian Sahibs' wit, whilst we remained unmoved and silent.

After a great deal of effort the Magistrate Class One permitted fourteen witnesses to appear on our behalf. So, the list was marked off and summons issued accordingly. I did not meet with any of the witnesses as I wanted each one of them to give their unbiased opinion about the short story and I, in the process, find out my exact position.

The witnesses on whom the summons had been served had to reach the court rather early in the morning. I felt extremely embarrassed as all arrived at the expense of their daily tasks and stood around waiting for hours. Though we were the accused, their position was no better than ours. We stood inside the court, in the dock, while they stood outside the Court room, leaning against the iron railing, waiting to be summoned into the court.

My friend Sheikh Saleem's condition was pitiable. He was in the habit of imbibing daily, morning and evenings. The whole day he yawned. Eventually he could no longer tolerate this state and started bringing a hip flask wherefrom he would take a sip or two ever so often. He did not have any connection with literature but when he spoke to others he would say: "After all what is obscenity? I cannot believe, even though I have not read it, that the short story "THANDA GOSHT" is obscene. Manto is an artiste."

The first witness from our side was Syed Abid Ali Abid, M.A.LLB., Principal Dyal Singh College Lahore. While testifying he said: "I have read "THANDA GOSHT" in the magazine "JAVED"- it is a piece of literature. I have read all of Manto's writings. After Prem Chand, amongst the short story writers of any consequence, Saadat Hassan Manto has achieved a special position - in this short story the main thrust of the untoward action of the character Esher Singh is that he was punished by turning impotent due to a psychological trauma."

On a question from the Court Abid Sahib responded: "Everyone from Wali to Ghalib wrote at times what may be termed obscene. Literature is never obscene if it is classified as literary work."

The Prosecution raised a question whether literature was not intended to be about life? Abid Sahib responded by saying that: "I have already stated that literature is a criticism of life and this statement includes the answer to your question. The words and deeds of every decent person mean something. But not all humans are decent. All words and acts can be good or bad in the eyes of the society. But in order to determine good or bad acts there can be many standards." In response to another question from the Prosecution, Abid Sahib says: "All my children, male and female, have read the short story. I have often discussed the subject of 'Sex,' in a literary context, with one of my daughters, a student of fourth year, as it is part of her curriculum. All my exchange of views on this short story with other writers of literature resulted in a wide acclaim for the same."

The second witness for the defense was Mr. Ahmad Saeed, Professor of Psychology, Dyal Singh College, Lahore. He in his statement said: "The short story "THANDA GOSHT" is not obscene. It highlights a very important sexual issue." According to him, the word obscene has no roots and in fact is man-created. People who were already sick in their heads may have been adversely affected by reading "THANDA GOSHT."

The third witness was Doctor Khalifa Abdul Hakeem, M.A.LLB., PHD, Ex - Director Education, Kashmir. In his statement he declared that: "The Psychology of every human is composed of good and evil. It is the job of a litterateur to bring out these facets in such manner that will assist in an understanding of the realities of the character's life. A bad character should be presented in such manner that on reading his evil deeds a feeling of disgust is created. In the short story under debate the character of Esher Singh creates an intense feeling of hate and disgust. The characterization is absolutely correct. Such characters although physically strong are most likely to succumb psychologically to impotency in certain given traumatic conditions."

The statements of the three witnesses were recorded at one hearing. Since the statements were lengthy and each and every word had to be written down by the Magistrate himself, he would become irritated and remark that he was a magistrate and not a clerk of the court. Notwithstanding such outbursts he continued to perform his duty.

During the course of the hearing an amusing incident took place. I was standing in the dock holding a box of "Craven - A" cigarettes when the magistrate saw it and in a scolding manner told me that this was not my home but a court room. I respectfully replied that I was not smoking. He got very annoyed and ordered me to keep quiet and place the box of cigarettes in my pocket. I obeyed, but then the Magistrate proceeded to pick a cigarette out of his own box of cigarettes which was lying on the table in front of him and lit up. I remained standing in the dock inhaling the smoke of his cigarette.

At the next hearing Mr. Tassaduq Hussain Khalid did not turn up as a family member was unwell. He did not appear at the next hearing either as his son was returning from England that day and he had proceeded to Karachi to receive him. The three of us were extremely puzzled as to what to do next, so I humbly requested the Court to postpone the hearing that day as our lawyer was not present. The Magistrate declined my request and ordered the proceedings to continue. I was very agitated.

The next witness, Doctor Saeedullah, M.A., LLB, PHD, DSC, was summoned. He was currently with the Pakistan Air Force as a civilian officer. I wondered what to do. The fact that most of the elders in my family were lawyers, father a judge and two elder brothers' barristers, some of their legal acumen had probably rubbed onto me as well. So I took the place of Mr. Tassaduq Hussain Khalid and got my witness number four

Doctor Saeedullah on the way to making his statement. The magistrate sahib interrupted at every point telling me that I could not put a question the way I did, or that I could not ask some thing, but I carried on regardless.

The Doctor had just about delivered half of his statement when four young lawyers wearing black coats, alert looking and smartly attired, walked into the court room and went and stood next to Doctor Saeedullah. One of them, slightly darker than the other two and with a slim moustache, came and stood right next to me, leaning patiently against the dock. A little while later when I paused for breath, he whispered into my ears, "Mr. Manto, may I plead your case, please?" Without giving the matter any second thought I said to him "Yes you may." So, as the slim moustached young lawyer took up his position to plead, he was asked by the Magistrate as to how come he was in the court. The lawyer smilingly responded "My Lord I am his lawyer. Isn't that so Mr. Manto?" I nodded my head in agreement. The proceedings recommenced. The other three lawyer friends of the slim moustached one also started participating. Their enthusiasm reflected an alluring youthfulness which is generally found in college-going students.

The Magistrate got irritated and asked the three of them as to why they were intruding in the proceedings, to which they replied "My Lord we are the lawyers of the accused, isn't that so Mr. Manto?" I again nodded my head in agreement.

A synopsis of Doctor Saeedullah's statement is presented herewith. He said: "After reading the story "THANDA GOSHT" I myself turned into "THANDA GOSHT."

Depression and sadness engulfed me. This story does not create any kind of a sexual arousal. The writer, to emphasize the character of Esher Singh, used abuses twice or thrice. It is possible that the author may have considered this correct. But the abuses have been worded in such manner that they do not appear to be abuses. If the expletives used by Esher Singh were to be considered as such even then I would not consider this story to be obscene. An abuse may or may not be vulgar. If the writer is a proper craftsman he would never use an expletive without cause. The use of expletives in this story is an example of good craftsmanship."

When the Prosecutor, a refined, mild-mannered gentleman, elegantly stiff necked, wearing rimless glasses, which he took off and put on repeatedly, made a cynical remark, Doctor Sahib retorted so loudly that Sufi Tabassum Sahib seated in the adjoining room, jumped off his chair and rushed out. Anyway the matter was resolved.

The Prosecutor, whose name probably was Mohammed Iqbal, enquired of Doctor Sahib: "Various writers, based upon the genre of their writing, have been awarded various honorifics, for example, Rashid Al Khairi is known as a painter of melancholy, Iqbal as an artisan of reality and Khwaja Hassan Nizami as nature's craftsman. How would you....." Doctor Sahib interrupted Mr. Iqbal mid-speech and said: "I award the honorific of an artiste of life to the author of "THANDA GOSHT.""

Now it was the turn of Colonel Faiz Ahmed Faiz, Editor Pakistan Times. He, in his statement, declared: "In my opinion the story is not obscene. To single out a word or two in a story and call the entire text obscene does not make sense. When one critically reviews a story the entire text should be and must be kept in view. The nakedness of anything is not an argument for it being obscene. I believe that the author of this story has not indulged in obscenity but has failed to maintain the high standards of literature, as he has not presented a satisfactory analysis of the basic problems of life."

On cross examination Faiz Sahib said 'He was kissing me' are words that he would consider absolutely valid for use provided the subject of the story permits that. 'Smothered me with his kisses,' 'Slobbered the breasts by repeatedly sucking them,' are words that may not be parliamentary but from a literary perspective are absolutely permissible."

After Faiz Sahib had finished, Sufi Ghulam Mustafa Tabassum, Professor Government College Lahore, came to testify. In his statement he said: "The story "THANDA GOSHT" does not have a corrupting influence on people's morality. Perhaps some phrases in it, if considered on a stand alone basis, may be obscene and others not. The trend established by using human sexuality as a theme in our literature is a move in the right direction." Responding to the cross examination, Sufi Sahib said, "Any story or literary work cannot be obscene as long as the objective of the writer is to write a piece of literature. Literature for the sake of literature is never obscene."

Iqbal Sahib impatiently and repeatedly took off and put on his rimless glasses with the intention of bringing Sufi Sahib round to saying what he wanted to hear. But Sufi Sahib was no novice as he had been imparting education for the last twenty years and could not be trapped in Iqbal Sahibs' web. On one occasion Sufi Sahib blatantly said: "Look here Sir. You may turn and twist but I will only say what I have to say." Iqbal Sahib inquired: "If the effect of any writing, story or literary work is depravation of morality even though the intention of the writer was not to create such an effect, would you or not term such a story obscene?" It was quite clear as to what Iqbal Sahib was insinuating, but Sufi Sahib smilingly retorted: "No. Because the words will be interpreted by the reader's own thinking and not by the meaning intended to be conveyed by the author. Creative writing is the result of a writer's self-thought which is meant to be shared with others." Iqbal Sahib persisted with another question: "If such writing has a bad influence on peoples' character would the responsibility thereof lie with the writer or not?" Sufi sahib immediately retorted: "The writer will not be held guilty." Iqbal Sahib, by now apparently fed up, asked: "How would you explain a writing which is depraved?" Sufi Sahib responded: "That writing which is intended to cause depravation of character."

Iqbal Sahib reset the rimless spectacles on his nose, lowered his stiff neck a bit and ended the cross examination.

Doctor I. Lateef, Head of the Psychology Department, F.C. College, Lahore, was summoned next. I had heard of him but had never seen or met him before. During the course of Sufi Sahib's testimony he was seated near Mian Saeed Sahib, holding the special edition of the magazine "JAVED" in his hand. I had not paid any attention to him. When he proceeded to give his testimony I looked at him closely. Though dark colored it was his swirling moustache which caught my attention. He put aside the magazine and started his statement: "I have just now read the story "THANDA GOSHT." It has been published in a wrong magazine. What I mean is that if it had not been published in a popular magazine but rather in a scientific one as a case study on the subject of sexual potency or impotency, it would never have been accused of obscenity. In my opinion the words that have already been pointed out could be termed indecent in conversation but as part of a case study they would assume great importance."

God knows what happened when, suddenly, Doctor Lateef inquired as to who Mr. Manto was? I admitted to being him. The Doctor's moustache stirred feverishly but he did not say anything to me and proceeded with his testimony. The lawyer whispered in my ear: "Manto Sahib, this witness of yours appears to have turned hostile. You can now cross examine him." I tell him to forget it. But the lawyer went ahead and cross examined him. In reply to a question Doctor Lateef said: "The short story should not have been published in a magazine that could be read by the young and old and females because such writing causes these passionate minds to be provoked."

After the cross examination ended, Doctor Sahib came towards me and shook my hand and said: "As you had asked me to testify the least you could have done is to have met me earlier." I smilingly responded: "God willing, I shall now certainly do so." He re-shook my hands and departed.

Now I would like to say a few words about the four young lawyers who had in a rather dramatic fashion burst onto these proceedings. Sheikh Khurshid Ahmed was the one with the slim moustache, a sharp nose and slightly dark colored. Coffee House was incomplete without his presence. The other three were named Mr. Mazhur ul Haq, Mr. Sardar Mohammed Iqbal and Mr. Ijaz Ahmed Khan. These persons, on finding out in the Bar Room that I was trying to conduct my own case and that too in a disturbed frame of mind, rushed out to help me. I thanked them profusely. Sheikh Khurshid Ahmed said: "there is no need for the thanks. But kindly appreciate me for not having read, let alone even seeing, your story "THANDA GOSHT." We all laughed and he added: "I will be quite glad to place a wager that neither has Mr. Iqbal."

So far seven witnesses had testified on our behalf. When Sheikh Khurshid Sahib requested the court to permit him to produce the remaining witnesses, his request was turned down. The Magistrate was perhaps a little apprehensive and felt that the scales had tilted in our favour, so he decided to invite four witnesses on the courts behalf, namely, Moulana Tajwar Najibabadi, Agha Shorish Kashmiri, Abu Saeed Bazmi and Doctor Mohammed Din Taseer.

However, many hearing dates went by but these four individuals could not be assembled on the same day. Eventually at one hearing they were all present. After formal greetings had been exchanged with Tajwar Sahib, he started lecturing that I (Manto) indulge in writing vulgar, obscene and absurd short stories. I kept quiet because it was pointless arguing with the Moulana.

Agha Shorish met me enthusiastically, while Abu Saeed Bazmi asked me for a cigarette, lit it up and started pacing back and forth outside the court room. When the call went out they presented themselves in the Court. The Proceedings commenced with the first court witness, namely, Shams ul Ulema Moulana Ehsan Ullah Khan Tajwar Najibabadi, Professor Dyal Singh College, Lahore. He opined that: "The reading of "THANDA GOSHT'" cannot be heard or appreciated in a mosque, or a gathering of persons. If any body dare read it, then, so be it on his head. In forty years of literary life I have never seen such a filthy and obscene article." I posed a few questions to the Moulana to which he replied: "The first time I started reading this short story was in Dyal Singh College, but I could not finish it. I read a little and understanding it to be absurd put it away. The narration pertaining to the wedding of Nasim and Taj ul Malook in 'Masnavi Gulzar Naseem,' was in conflict with morality. All those parts of the writings in 'Fasana Ajaib,' ' Masnavi Bahar-e-Ishq,' ' Masnavi Faraib –e- Ishq' and 'Alif Laila' that are obscene are in fact obscene. I have not read the tale of Khanum and Kaneez in 'Masnavi Moulana Rumi'."

I wished to tease the Moulana more, but considered it to be uncivil. I let him go after a few more questions. Next to be called was Agha Shorish Kashmiri, son of Agha Nizamuddin, Editor, weekly "Chataan", wearing a huge grin on his face visible through his bushy moustache. He looked and smiled openly at me and proceeded to record his testimony.

He said: "In so far as my knowledge and feelings are concerned I have not formed a good opinion of "THANDA GOSHT." Keeping the society and family that I belong to in view, I would not print such an article in my magazine. My school of thought cannot live with it." In reply to a question raised by the Prosecutor he added: "It will promote vulgarity particularly in those people who have a tendency for immoral behavior."

Agha Sahib was not subjected to cross examination from our side. Abu Saeed Bazmi, Editor "Ehsaan," Lahore, came next and stated that he found the story immoral. He added: "The meaning and intent of the story is objectionable." I enquired of Bazmi whether it was correct that a case against him was pending in this particular court. When he replied in the affirmative, the Magistrate incredulously enquired "In my Court?" Bazmi Sahib again replied in the affirmative. The Magistrate started scratching his head with his pen, lit up his pipe and engaged himself in his work.

The last Court witness was Doctor Taseer Sahib, Principal Islamia College Lahore. In his testimony he said: "The story from a literary perspective is worthless. But it is a piece of literature. In so far as the highlighted words in the story are concerned some are an essential part of it others not. There are some words that can be referred to as indecent. But I will not refer to them as obscene as I am not clear about the concept of obscenity. In my opinion, those people who have a tendency towards immoral behavior, for them there is a sexual direction in the story. A person who does not have a perverted mind will after reading this story have a feeling of disgust for sexuality not an incentive to indulge in immoral sex. "THANDA GOSHT" means a dead female. I consider this story a run of the mill sex-based story which cannot debase sexual morality."

The Court Proceedings had thus reached the end and only the announcement of the formal decision remained, although Mian A.M. Saeed Sahib had hinted repeatedly at what it was going to be during the hearings. Sheikh Khurshid Ahmed was quite sure that all of us would be fined. The date of the announcement of the decision was fixed as January 16 (of current year). Naseer Anwar appeared totally unruffled. During the course of the entire proceedings he kept smiling. But Arif Abdul Mateen, at most times, looked extremely worried which perhaps was due to the fact that his elderly father was in a state of panic.

Soon after the witnesses had ended their testimony I submitted my written statement to the Court. I remember distinctly that after reading it the Magistrate said: "This statement alone provides sufficient cause to penalize the accused." The written statement was as follows:

"I am the author of the short story "THANDA GOSHT" printed in the monthly "JAVED" Lahore, which is considered by the Prosecution as vulgar and obscene. I vehemently differ with this view as this story, from any perspective, is not as alleged.

One can say a lot about obscenity. But it is an established fact that literature can never, never be obscene. If the story "THANDA GOSHT" is excluded from the ambit of literature, then a question may arise regarding it being obscene or not. But this story is the creation of a littérateur who holds a position of eminence in modern literature. The evidence of this fact is his writings and various articles on his literary prowess that have been published in nearly all literary magazines.

Before this particular time, some of my writings were considered obscene on three different occasions and each time I was tried and sentenced, but every time, on submission of an appeal against the decisions to the Session Court, I and my writings were cleared of the charges of obscenity. The words written in a judgment by Mr. M.R.Bhattia, Additional Session Judge, in one of the trials, demand attention: "The fact is worth consideration that such people have appeared as witnesses for the defence who are extremely well known because of their pre-eminence as scholars of Urdu language. For example, Khan Bahadur Abdur Rehman Chughtai, Mr. K.L. Kapoor, Professor DAV College, Rajinder Singh Bedi and Doctor I. Lateef, Professor FC College. All of these people are of the opinion that the story "BOO" did not contain anything which could cause sexual provocation. In fact they thought that the story was progressive and indicative of modern Urdu writing. Even the Prosecution witness number four, Bashir, during the course of the cross examination admitted that the writing was not a cause of bad influence on human morality. The subordinate court had expressed displeasure with the fun loving life style of the Hindustani youth and grieved that the old character of the Hindustanis, as a whole, was being destroyed. The Judge in the Subordinate Court also recounted the good deeds for which we Hindustanis were once famous and counseled that new fads should be stopped. It appears that the views of the honorable subordinate court are not progressive. We have to move with the times. A thing of beauty is a joy forever. Art, wherever found, must be respected, whether it is in a painting or in the form of a sculpture. It is an absolute gift for the society even if the subject is abstract. The same principle applies to the writings in question.

When the renowned and acclaimed artistes and writers have testified in favour of the accused, the decision is thus taken for granted. The story in question is not of such nature whereupon criticism can be attributed to it in a court of law. Therefore we have no issues in accepting the appeal. The fine if already paid shall be refunded. The appellants are therefore declared exonerated of all alleged guilt."

It is apparent from the above decision that Art cannot be obscene and an artistic work should not be the subject of criticism in a Court of Law. A piece of literary work or literature can be of an acceptable standard or not. This may be so because the artist may not be able to achieve the high standard every time. Every short story penned by a short story writer may not be of the high standard expected of him.

The literary stature of "THANDA GOSHT" can be argued about. It may be said that this story is not of the same caliber as my other short stories. This is the job of literary critics and it is their right to do so. But under no circumstances can this short story be accused of obscenity. This is so because in fictional literature, the story created by the writer, good or bad or howsoever it may be regarded, is still an addition to literature. In order to further clear my position let us examine the short story in question and find out if it has an obscene aspect to it.

The short story "THANDA GOSHT" is obviously only a story. The background to it is clearly the recent riots and disturbances. In fact such occurrences are an outcome of human psychological behavior that also applies to sexuality.

There are two characters in the story, Esher Singh and his mistress Kalwant Kaur. The two are an epitome of very rustic, coarse uneducated Sikhs. Both are physically strong. It could be said that Kalwant Kaur's physical needs could only be satisfied by as strong and potent an individual as Esher Singh. They had a very satisfying sexual relationship. But there came a time when Kalwant Kaur started feeling that there was a change in Esher Singh. He was no longer as passionate in his love making as before. He had become somewhat indifferent towards her. She thought perhaps he had entered into a relationship with some other woman. But the fact was that Esher Singh was suffering from a major psychological trauma and as a result had become impotent. During the lootings and killings, he, after having done the business of slaying innocents, had abducted from amongst them a young Muslim girl to satisfy his sexual lust. But when he attempted to commit the act he discovered that the girl had died while on his shoulders as she was being carted away and there was nothing left of her but a cold, naked cadaver that now lay in front of him. His sexual urge was now thwarted by a piece of ice cold meat. The psychological effect of this on Esher Singh was such that he turned impotent. Perhaps if Esher Singh had relationships with only frigid women or if he, himself, were a cold person the extent of the psychological trauma may not have been that much. But he has been portrayed as a sexually strong individual who had an ongoing relationship with a woman who also appeared to be his match. This is why the impact of the stated incident was so great on him.

It is also worth noting that the killings and pillage that he indulged in on a daily basis, during the course of which he butchered many humans, had absolutely no psychological impact on him. His conscience was never affected by this slaughter but when he hovered atop the lifeless body of a girl he lost his sexuality.

Whatever is written in the text of the story is obviously not obscene. Even the title of the story is such that it cannot inflame the sexual passions of a reader. How can the incident that adversely affected Esher Singh's life cause sexual titillation in the reader? Esher Singh has his own style of conversation. Thousands of people in their daily lives use the same words that the author has made Esher Singh speak. His actions were not unnatural. The same can be said of Kalwant Kaur.

The Prosecution lawyer has highlighted the fact that the dialogues of Esher Singh were replete with expletives. I will not discuss the psychology behind the usage of expletives here but only state the fact that the words construed by the lawyer to be abuses are in fact not abuses.

I shall present here two examples of abuse. The famous poet of Urdu, Mirza Ghalib, in a note addressed to Mirza Shabuddin Khan Sahib wrote: 'God knows which son of a rapist has submitted the verses that you have sent to me. Even if they are found to be balanced you may assume that the original lines have been ruthlessly mauled by a God forsaken rapist and absurdity penned instead.' (URDU –A- MUAALA Page 217).

In another letter addressed to Mirza Shabuddin he writes: 'The clown of a Qazi here is an asshole (a chootiya.)' (URDU –A- MUAALA Page 218).

We are done with examples of abuse. But if a person during the course of a conversation says that he is a proper asshole, as the person he was looking for was right there whilst he searched all over for him in Lahore, then the use of the word asshole is not an abuse. In our circles 'Saala' is considered to be an abuse but this word has no significance in the Bombay dialect. There the daily conversation is replete with sentences such as:

'My father, saala, is a very good man.'

'Saala, I have made a mistake.'

'What kind of a saala talk is this?'

Abuses referring to mothers and sisters are openly used in ordinary conversation in U.P. and Punjab, and no one takes umbrage at that. Certain abuses become the catch phrases of certain individuals. Esher Singh also uses certain abuses as his catch phrase. Therefore the insistence of the Prosecution on this issue is futile.

Another very important matter must be kept in view. One should not expect an illiterate, coarse, ill mannered boor like Esher Singh to talk in a sophisticated and eloquent style. If the author had made him speak in a decent and civil style then the story would have lost the realism that it reflects. In fact I would go to the extent of saying that if this course were followed the short story would have assumed an indecent, contorted appearance which would then have fallen from the levels of literature to the depths of nonsense.

The question really is why should not things be presented as they are? Why should a rag be referred to as brocade? Why should a mound of filth be depicted as a bed of sweet smelling flowers? Does denial of reality make us better people? Never. Therefore the criticism on Esher Singh's character and manner of discourse holds no meaning whatsoever.

Esher Singh may be a perverted mind. The title of the short story may be atrocious. But after reading it can one not sense a trace of humanity creeping into the black heart of Esher Singh because of his abominable deed. And this is a healthy sign, as the author of this short story is not disenchanted with either humans or humanity. If the author had not created the psychological reaction that he did in Esher Singh's mind and heart then certainly "THANDA GOSHT" would have been a dangerous story.

I am sorry that those writings that inform humans that even if they turn into beasts they still cannot be excluded from the ambit of humanity are being understood as sexually provocative and obscene. And it is rather droll that in this short story a human is hugely penalized by whatever humanity was left in him. It is to be noted that Esher Singh was never bothered by his slashed throat but only by one thing, right until his last gasps that he was about to commit rape on a cold dead carcass.

The well known author of France, Flaubert, was prosecuted because of charges of obscenity levelled against his novel 'Madame Bovary'. The lawyer for the defence during the course of his impressive statement remarked: 'Gentlemen! This book which according to the learned Counsel for Prosecution has been accused of sexual provocation is the result of the wide reading and reflective thought of Monsieur Flaubert. He has drawn our attention through nature's sobriety towards topics that are sombre and melancholy. He is not the kind of person as made out by the Prosecution attorney repeatedly in his statement, accusing him of sensationalizing different facets of life. I shall repeat again that Flaubert by nature is extremely sober, serious and perhaps even melancholy.'

I can only say this for myself that I belong to an honorable family. It is a mere coincident that my profession is to write and by virtue of my nature, education and training, I have to date never presented cheap and lurid literature. Any one who has any connection with modern Urdu literature knows of my literary stature well.

The short story "THANDA GOSHT" may not have the seriousness and sobriety that was Flaubert's nature but it cannot be denied that it is not full of sadness and when it is a matter of melancholy then the question of sexuality does not arise. Let us now also look at the short story from a different perspective namely the intentions of the author. In the Court of Rai Sahib Lala Sant Ram, during the course of the trial of my story "DUHWAAN," (" SMOKE"), I , in my testimony as the accused, had said: 'In writing , speaking, poetry, sculpture and painting if some one is looking for obscenity, the first thing is to look for the intention. If this intention is present, or even a shade thereof, then that speech, poetry that sculpture is totally obscene.'

Such an intention or inkling thereof cannot be attributed to the short story under discussion. I have earlier on analyzed the story and this clearly brings out the fact that the writer did not have any contrary ideas or intentions except presenting a psychological reality in its exactness through the medium of the short story. If after reading the short story "THANDA GOSHT" the feelings of any reader are aroused then that person must immediately consult a psychiatrist. In the testimony during the hearing of "SMOKE" I had stated: 'Only someone physically and emotionally ill and a retard can be influenced wrongly. The poet pens his poetry, the story writer writes his story and the painter creates his painting only for those who are morally, mentally, emotionally and physically healthy.' My short stories are meant for such people, normal people, for whom a woman's breast is no more than a breast and who do not look at the relationship between man and woman as something strange. The short story "THANDA GOSHT," like other literary works, is meant for healthy minds and hearts and not for those who look for sexuality even in innocent and pious things. If any person derives sexual excitement from the movement of a machine then would it be right to condemn the machine or its movement for causing a sexual arousal? There certainly are people in this world who seek sexual enjoyment even in the holy books. All such people must be medically treated.

In America Judge Woolsey adjudicating for the renowned author James Joyce in the obscenity charge against his book 'Ulysses' wrote: 'Whether a particular book would tend to excite such impulses and thoughts must be tested by the Court's opinion as to its effect on a person with average sex instincts -- what the French would call 'l'homme moyen sensuel' -- who plays, in this branch of legal inquiry, the same role of hypothetical reagent as does the 'reasonable man' in the law of torts and 'the man learned in the art' on questions of invention in patent law.' Therefore before taking a decision in the matter of the short story "THANDA GOSHT" the court must examine how the reading of the said short story may affect the mind and heart of a person with average sexual emotions and feelings.

The decision by the court in the obscenity charge against the renowned American author Erskine Caldwell's book 'God's Little Acre' stated that: 'the intention of the writer was to paint a realistic picture. In painting such pictures it is but inevitable that certain details are included. And since such details do have a deep relationship with life's sexual aspects therefore they are explained very distinctly. Therefore the Court cannot rule that such descriptions should abinitio not be written or painted. The language used by the characters may be vile and provocative but the court cannot demand of the writer that such uncouth characters speak in a civilized tongue.'

The short story "THANDA GOSHT" is a true reflection. There is no ambiguity in it. In a very clear and direct manner the human psychology has been described. If there is dirt and filth in it then it ought not to be attributed to the author but the mental capacity of the characters in the story.

Words, if presented in isolation rather than as a piece of writing to people, may seem obscene and thus not result in a correct assessment of the writing. The publication of such words individually may become objectionable in the same way as some of the words used in the writings of Ghalib, Mir, Aristophanes, Chaucer and indeed the Holy Book. Notwithstanding this, to understand any writing it has to be read as a whole.

In the end I may be permitted to state that the Prosecution has failed to provide a literary criticism of my short story "THANDA GOSHT." If this had happened then I would have been delighted. If the story lacked in any technical respect, or the description was dubious or the grammar was incorrect then I would have stood informed and learnt something from the criticism. But here I stand in the Prisoner's Dock accused of the very serious crime of using my writing to arouse sexual emotions of the people. What else can you expect to pour out of my heart except protests?

It is indeed strange that the mind of the reader, after reading "THANDA GOSHT", is presumed not to have been overawed by fear and hate but is supposed to have been sexually aroused. And it is even stranger that the severe punishment of Esher Singh is purported to have created sexual stirrings in the minds of the readers."

January 16 arrived. Shaikh Saleem was apprehensive. Because of this reason he had started drinking too much. Naseer Anwar as usual was unperturbed. Dear Arif Abdul Mateen's throat had dried up even more. On the morning of 16th January with five hundred Rupees in my pocket I started walking towards the District Courts. Shaikh Saleem was already there and had started drinking since early morning. His bottle was in his pocket and he appeared agitated. However, he continued to reassure me and not to worry and that everything would turn out alright. I would smile, listening to him.

Soon Naseer Anwar and Arif Abdul Mateen arrived. Arif in an extremely concerned manner asked of me "Manto Sahib what do you think is going to happen?" I responded by saying whatever happens will be according to God's will.

The Magistrate had also reached the Court, but there was no indication of the decision being announced. Time passed by and soon it was noon. Our stomachs became bloated with water that we had been drinking but we were not summoned. A while later one of my informers came to tell me that the decision was ready but Mr. A.M. Saeed desired some amendment in it. Few moments later we found out that Mian Sahib had disappeared from his room and that he had not touched any other case since morning. Somebody said that he was in a state of anguish. Anyway one heard as many opinions as there were mouths. The informer came back bringing confirmed information that he had now had an opportunity to quickly glance through the decision and in particular the last few lines. He told me that I was being fined and sentenced to imprisonment as it was written against my name "And sentenced to undergo..." But the spaces thereafter were blank. The others would only be fined. He promised to return after making arrangements for a guarantor.

I started to think about the term of imprisonment. Would it be for a month or two or just a few days? I apprised Shaikh Khurshid Sahib of the matter who immediately started preparing the bail bond. He said to me: "Do not worry Manto Sahib; the sentence shall not be for more than ten or twelve days." But on reflection added in a worried tone: "I hope he doesn't refuse to grant you bail."

On hearing this I became extremely worried because the magistrate's attitude right from the beginning was hostile. But then nothing certain could be said. I agitatedly kept turning the matter in my mind. Eventually I could not keep it all to myself and shared the entire conversation with Shaikh Saleem. My mind felt a little lighter but the poor Shaikh become even more aggravated than before. However, to appease me he said: "Do not worry, Brother. I will hire a taxi and come to see you in the jail. Money can do anything. You will not be in discomfort. I know how to handle such issues. I think you should have a drink." I responded by politely thanking him. He assured me that he would make certain that drinks would be served to me in prison.

On hearing this I laughed. It was now one o'clock in the afternoon. Shaikh Saleem, Naseer Anwar and I sat on the grass lawn in front of the Government College hostel and quickly ate "Alu Cholay" (Potatoes and chick peas) lest we may be summoned by the Court any minute.

I had repeatedly indicated to both Naseer Anwar and Arif Abdul Mateen that they should arrange for the fine expected to be imposed so that at the time no further embarrassment should be caused. Shaikh Saleem kept on imbibing and creating schemes of how to reach me in jail and what sources to use to ensure my comfort therein.

Mr. Mushtaq Ahmed, my informer, had brought, from amongst his wealthy friends, one Mr. Sharif, to act as my guarantor who too was getting bored whilst waiting for the Magistrate. Shaikh Saleem was annoyed that in his presence why was it necessary to get an outsider to act as a guarantor. I told him that if he was that interested in being the guarantor there were two other individuals who needed help. Shaikh Sahib smiled after listening to me, took another sip and again became busy in scheming. He appeared very worried about Manto's evening being spoilt.

It had turned five o'clock in the evening. By this time our concerns and worries had increased manifold. Shaikh Naseer, however, continued to appear totally unruffled as if nothing was going to happen and we all were impressed with his apparent posture. Arif Abdul Mateen's throat had gone so dry that he had stopped talking. At five thirty we were eventually called Immediately Shaikh Khurshid Sahib was informed and he returned post haste. We were now all present in the Court.

Mian A.M.Saeed, with his fountain pen between his teeth and the judgment papers in front of him, was engrossed in deep thought. Shaikh Khurshid's face reflected the tensions within him, my pulse was throbbing rapidly, Shaikh Saleem's face had turned very pale and Arif Abdul Mateen was repeatedly trying to wet his lips with a very dry tongue. Naseer Anwar however still looked undeterred.

The Press Reporters were present, ready with paper and pencils in their hands and awaiting the decision anxiously. A few more minutes elapsed in complete silence and then Mian A.M.Saeed noisily cleared his throat, removed the fountain pen from his mouth, dipped it into the inkpot, turned over the papers on which the judgment was written several times and then proceeded to fill in the blanks. Thereafter he pronounced his judgment on me – three months rigorous imprisonment and Rupees Three hundred fine – in case of failure to pay the fine a further twenty one days (21) days rigorous imprisonment

Shaikh Saleem went even more pale than before but tried to comfort me through the movement of his eyes as if saying do not worry as he would sort out the matters at the Jail.

I started wondering whether the Magistrate would accept my bail or not. A little later Mian A.M.Saeed filled in the other blank spaces and pronounced his verdict on the other two accused – A fine of Rs. three hundred each and in case of failure to pay the fine twenty one days rigorous imprisonment.

I paid the fine. Shaikh Khurshid Sahib presented the bail bond to the Magistrate who immediately declared that: "If I accept his bail then the entire purpose of the sentence comes to naught." Shaikh Khurshid argued that: "You may be right but the accused has paid the fine, which on appeal against your decision will be returned to him. But the three days of his life, prior to release on bail, that my client shall spend in Jail shall be lost to him forever and that too before the acceptance of his appeal." It was a very reasonable argument but Mian A.M.Saeed remained unmoved momentarily before accepting my bail papers in a very condescending manner.

Arif Abdul Mateen's father paid up his fine. That left Naseer Anwar who when asked responded most casually that he did not at present have any money. The Magistrate ordered that he should be handcuffed and sent to prison. Naseer Anwar kept standing without uttering a word. I had only Rupees two hundred left. I requested Choudhry Nazir, owner "NAYA IDARA", to arrange for the balance rupees one hundred but he was unable to do so. The police constable with handcuffs in hand stood right behind Naseer Anwar. Their clang resounded in the court room. Outside, the police van had arrived. All arrangements were thus complete.

At last it was Khurshid Sahib who came to the rescue when he in a most appropriate and respectful manner pleaded with Mian A.M.Saeed to accept the bail bond of Naseer Anwar and assured him that the fine would be deposited the next morning. The Magistrate accepted the plea. Now it was a question of who would be the guarantor. No one stepped up. Suddenly Shaikh Saleem, who was by now completely soused, in a sad tone addressed Shaikh Khurshid Sahib and volunteered to be the guarantor for Naseer Sahib. My heart started beating faster. If the Court found out that Shaikh Saleem was in a drunken state, would any one be prepared to bail him out? I was sure that he would then be arrested and the whole affair would come to naught. Fearing this outcome I went out of the Court room but repeatedly looked in to see whether Shaikh Saleem had been arrested or not. Anyway sanity prevailed.

Naseer Anwar's bail bond was accepted. Shaikh Saleem came out of the Court room and embraced me only to start weeping whilst exclaiming that God had saved his brother. He then pulled the bottle out of his pocket and put it to his lips and finished it off. He then declared that all should proceed to the wine shop forthwith lest it closed up for the day.

Naseer Anwar appeared very satisfied and grateful. He repeatedly thanked Shaikh Saleem, who turned round and said to him: "There is no need to thank me. I did my duty as you are a friend's friend."

We soon started preparing for the appeal in the Sessions Court. We applied to obtain an official copy of Mian A.M.Saeed Sahib's decision. When we did not meet success 'wheels' were applied where after the copy was rapidly provided. The decision penned in English ran as follows:

"DECISION: The Editor, Arif Abdul Mateen, and Publisher, Naseer Anwar, of an Urdu Magazine titled "JAVED" along with a writer Saadat Hassan Manto have been produced before me in connection with a case registered against them under Section 292 of the PPC. The last named is accused of being the author of an obscene short story titled "THANDA GOSHT" which has been published in a special issue of the afore stated magazine. The other two are accused of publishing the said short story.

The special issue of "JAVED" was published in March 1949. It came to the notice of Syed Ziauddin, translator Press Branch Government of Punjab, Prosecution witness number three, that it was his job to bring to the attention of the Government of Punjab, any printed matter that appeared obscene to him. In his view the short story "THANDA GOSHT" appearing in the special issue of the aforesaid magazine was obscene. Accordingly, he drew the attention of Punjab Government towards it and advised that a legal suit may be filed in this respect.

None deny the authorship of the story and its publication in the special issue. None deny that the first two accused are the Editor and Publisher of the magazine respectively. The only question that remains to be addressed therefore is whether the short story "THANDA GOSHT" is obscene or not.

The Prosecution has presented the special issue of the said magazine which is recorded as exhibit EX-P-F. The story that is the cause of this prosecution is printed on pages 88 to 93 of this issue. I have read this story very intently which is also the cause of its title and noticed that it contains a vulgar manner of speech and use of indecent abuses. I also felt that sexually provocative incidents and sexual innuendoes aplenty were part of the short story.

In order to decide whether a particular story is obscene or not, say this one for example, it is necessary to have a benchmark which would assist in determination of obscenity.

In the Hicklin Report (3 QB 1868) relating to an important court case on this very subject, Lord Cockburn on page 390 (or page 271) had laid out a test for judging obscenity. **"The test of obscenity is whether the intention of the matter charged as obscene is to deprave and corrupt those whose minds are susceptible to such immoral influences and into whose hands a publication of this sort may fall."**

It appears that all honorable courts of Hindustan have been following this standard. It also appears from this criterion that the prevalent definition of obscenity relates to the environment in which it is recognized. Matters that may be deemed harmful for the character of a Pakistani may not be deemed as such for a French person. Every society has its own standards of moral conduct and therefore issues that may be considered as a benchmark of morality in one society may be deemed immoral in another. Similarly the effect of some aspects of an expression may be different for people living in different societies even if such thoughts may be considered as morally depraved in other societies. Accordingly, the decision on whether the short story under discussion is obscene or not shall have to be taken in the context of the Pakistani standards of morality and the likely effects of such writing on the minds of the people living in this society. The standard laid down by Lord Cockburn is neither complete nor comprehensive. As is apparent from its interpretation it is only one test but there may be many other differing criteria. One of these is the intention, (as is to be found in the alleged material), that damages the morality of the readers. This criteria is also dependant on the readers own moral conduct.

The Prosecution initially presented five witnesses and closed its case. Prosecution witness (1) Mr. Mohammed Yaqub, Manager Kapoor Printing Press, (2) Shaikh Mohammed Tufail, (4) Mirza Mohammed Aslam and (5) Khuda Baksh testified on matters that had nothing to do with obscenity. Prosecution witness (3) Syed Ziauddin, in addition to explaining other matters expressed his opinion that the story under discussion is obscene. However, there is nothing available on record to establish that this witness could be considered as an expert litterateur. Therefore, in my opinion, in accordance with section 45 of the Law of Evidence, his testimony is not accepted. Hence in so far as the issue of Obscenity is concerned the case of the Prosecution as initially explained has become dependant on the opinion of the court and the inferences drawn from study of the objectionable material.

The accused have presented seven witnesses who are expert in literary matters. The thrust of their testimony was to establish that the short story under discussion was not obscene. At the conclusion of the testimony of the defense, the Prosecution requested that in view of the importance of the issue some more experts as witnesses of the court be allowed. In pursuance of equity four more experts were allowed to appear as witnesses of the court.

Most of the experts whether they appeared as defense or court witnesses opined in favour of either one or the other litigant. As has already been stated, the manner in which the expression 'obscenity' has been used in the penal code has a technical importance and it is for the Court to determine its relevance. The expert opinion was necessary only to that extent. It is for the Court to determine whether any particular matter meets the definition of obscenity in the light of the prevailing standards of literary expression, decent language, perversity, morality and immorality and how and to what extent it may affect the minds of it readers.

The defence witnesses number 1, Mr. Abid Ali Abid, number 2, Mr. Ahmed Saeed, number 3, Doctor Khalifa Abdul Hakeem, number 4, Doctor Saeedullah, number 5, Faiz Ahmed Faiz, number 6, Sufi Ghulam Mustafa Tabassum and number 7, Doctor I.Lateef are all men of letters. In their view as art is a reflection of life, therefore any artiste who depicts life in its true reality does not exceed the rights of expression. Accordingly they reason that a realistic expression of life cannot be obscene. They do not even consider the use of indecent and perverse phrases in the under discussion short story as a violation because that too represents such kind of expression which is used by that ilk of characters as presented in the said story. Some accepted that court witnesses number 1, Moulana Tajwar, number 2, Agha Shorish Kashmiri, number 3, Moulana Abu Saeed Bazmi and number 4, Doctor Taseer were also men of literature. The testimony of these witnesses establishes the fact that the short story under discussion is 'bad literature' and has been presented indecently.

The Defence witness number 7, Doctor I. Lateef, expressed an opinion that if the short story under discussion had been printed in a medical journal then it would be treated as a case study, but it appears unsuitable for a magazine that the public at large can read.

Defence witness number 5, Colonel Faiz Ahmed Faiz, has stated that although he would not consider the story obscene, it was not a good piece of literature. It contained several indecent phrases which could have been avoided.

Court witness number 1, Moulana Tajwar, condemned the story in very strong and clear words and said that in his forty year literary experience he had not come across anything more indecent.

Court witness number 4, Doctor Taseer opined that the story contains such matter which could corrupt the behavior of individuals in particular those who are affected by sexual greed and lust.

The standard of moral behavior in Pakistan can only be established in the light of koranic readings. It is said that indecency, sexuality, self centeredness and ambiguity are part of human life. If this standard is accepted as part of literature, as explained by the Defence witnesses, then a realistic expression of various facets of human life could be considered as good literature. But even then it would be a violation of the standards of morality in our society. The story written by the accused Saadat Hassan Manto characterizes a perverse man who desires his mistress, depicted as an over sexed person, in a most brutal and perverse manner to satisfy their mutual lust for sex. Use of sexual innuendos and indecent abuses has been made. The female private parts have been referred to in a most indecent manner whilst describing the sexual acts. The entire story is based on perverse sexual behavior. In fact sexual perversity is the basic thought of this story.

Literary and psychological experts can, in their own special way, accept certain reactions. However, in my opinion, the only impact of this short story on the minds of immature, young persons will be to deprave them and encourage indecency and perversity in their thought, action and expression.

The young persons, who read this story, will keep in mind the example set by Saadat Hassan Manto, the self-proclaimed renowned author, and therefore only be encouraged to adopt indecent behavior.

After a serious reading of the short story "THANDA GOSHT" I am satisfied that it contains character damaging material and that it contravenes the standards of morality applicable in this country of ours.

Accordingly, I declare the accused, Saadat Hassan Manto, guilty of presenting an obscene writing and in pursuance of section 212 PPC, sentence him to three months rigorous imprisonment and Rupees three hundred as fine. In case of failure to pay the fine he shall undergo a further twenty one days of confinement.

The other two accused, namely, Arif Abdul Mateen and Naseer Anwar, undeniably are the Editor and Publisher of the magazine in which the aforesaid story was printed. They are guilty of publishing a lewd piece of writing for the consumption of public at large and are also hit by the same section of the PPC. However, in their matter, in view of their young years they could have been overawed by the fact that the author of the story is a renowned literary figure and thus trusted him and accepted the story as a literary masterpiece. I therefore pronounce a softer punishment of a fine of Rupees three hundred for each of the two accused as I feel this would meet the requirements of justice. I accordingly order. In case of failure to pay the fine they shall undergo twenty one days of rigorous imprisonment.

SIGNED A.M. SAEED MAGISTRATE CLASS – 1, LAHORE"

On January 28, 1950, an appeal was filed against the decision in the Sessions Court. When the date of the hearing was announced, we presented ourselves in the court of Mr. Mehr ul Haq, Session Judge, Lahore. He, in view of the fact that he knew me and my family very well and also belonged to the same city (Amritsar), transferred the case to the Court of an Additional Sessions Judge, Mr. Joshua. On the second hearing we found out that the case had been reverted back to Mr. Mehr ul Haq's Court by Mr. Joshua on the plea that he did not understand the Urdu language very well. Mr. Mehr ul Haq after considerable thought decided to send the case to another Additional Sessions Judge, Mr. Inayat Ullah Khan. When we appeared before him he said to our lawyer that as the case before him was the first of its kind for him, he would like time to study it thoroughly. Accordingly he deferred the next hearing to a month later. Sheikh Khurshid Ahmed agreed. The date for arguments was then fixed as July 10.

When we came out of the Court room Shaikh Khurshid sahib said to me that the longish adjournment was good as it would give him enough time to fully prepare the case. He, however, was apprehensive of the fact that the case may have been transferred to a wrong person, a person, who is narrow minded, kept a beard and observed all religious rites. I told him to forget it as we could always go to the High Court. Shaikh Sahib during this time also requested me to guide him and pen a brief review on the short story "THANDA GOSHT."

In course of time I penned the following lines and gave them to him:

Prima facie the story revolves around the issue of psychology of sexual behavior but in fact it contains a very sophisticated message for human beings. It shows that even after reaching the extreme limits of cruelty and oppression, brutality and beastliness a human being does not lose its humanity. If Esher Singh had lost his humaneness then the thought of a dead woman would not have traumatized him so much to make him lose his manhood.

In order to emphasize the trauma from a psychological perspective and make it appear as realistic as possible, it was necessary that Esher Singh be shown as a man with greater sexual prowess than ordinary men. Therefore the author has repeatedly but succinctly done so in the story.

In order to further highlight the sexual aspect of Esher Singh's character and to make his tragedy acceptable to the reader the writer created the character of Kalwant Kaur who, similar to Esher Singh, was sexually more powerful and physically stronger than any ordinary women. If Esher Singh were an ordinary man and Kalwant Kaur an ordinary woman, the conclusion of the story "THANDA GOSHT" would have been totally different. An ordinary man who has had sexual relations with an ordinary woman could not have been psychologically traumatized by the cold and lifeless body of a girl in the same manner as a sexually potent and powerful character like Esher Singh. In fact so daunted was he by the experience that not only was he psychologically crushed by it but also became impotent.

Sex is a volcanic emotion. If this emotion is stirred within a human, the blood in its body starts boiling as does the body temperature. The human heart and mind reach a state of utter turmoil. The title of the under discussion short story is "THANDA GOSHT" which literally means ice cold meat and therefore should not create any rush of blood in the readers' mind and heart.

If the sexual urge in a woman is weak she is referred to as a frigid person, in other words, one who is unable to arouse a sexual desire in a man. The person responsible for creating the climax in the short story "THANDA GOSHT" is in the form of a dead, ice cold body of a girl. A gelid cadaver that drops heavily, just like a huge slab of ice, on the red-blooded aspirations of Esher Singh and also turns him ice cold. We can well imagine the kind of effect this climax would have on the readers of "THANDA GOSHT" who would not be as sexually hot-blooded as Esher Singh. In his testimony the defense witness, Doctor Saeedullah, M.A.LLB, PHD,DSC, very succinctly but effectively summed up his reaction by saying that after reading the short story "THANDA GOSHT" he himself had turned into a piece of cold flesh.

As far as normal individuals are concerned, it can be said without any fear of contradiction, that their reactions could be similar. It is a different matter that they may not be able to express their feelings in the same eloquent manner as Doctor Saeedullah. As far as abnormal persons are concerned, we will not talk about them except saying that there exist people who will not even leave a dead body alone.

The relationship between man and woman has not been presented in a scandalous manner in "THANDA GOSHT." The reason being, firstly, that this mannerism would have been in conflict with the real objective of the story. Secondly, because the author of this story is not a writer of sex. "THANDA GOSHT" does not present an intricate plot, or a cure for chronic constipation or a secret insight. "THANDA GOSHT" is a sorrowful picture of a man who still has a trace of humanity left in him despite his murderous activities. This trace, though, turns him impotent and the jealousy of his amorous beloved causes his extremely agonizing death. It is worth noting that whilst in the throes of death he is not bothered by anything other than the dead, ice cold body of the girl who was to be the subject of his lust.

Just before his death Esher Singh finally got a sense of his inhumane behavior. This sense was a ray of light in the barbarism that was surrounding him. The author writes "Blood had reached Esher Singh's tongue. When he ran his tongue over it and tasted his own blood a shiver ran down his body and he said to himself "And I, sister begat, have slaughtered six persons with this very *Kirpan.*"

Esher Singh had butchered six persons with his *Kirpan.* He had probably never even given a thought, until the psychological trauma that he underwent, to the fact that with his own hands he had slain six people. But now having tasted his own blood he ponders over the fact. It could be said that it had finally occurred to him that the *Kirpan* that had cut his throat was the same with which he had slaughtered six people. And do we not hear in the use of an abuse in his statement the sorrowful lament of his soul? Let us listen.

"And I, sister begat, have slaughtered six persons with this very *Kirpan.*" Esher Singh is feeling pain and anguish but is now conscious of what he had done. We cannot expect Esher Singh's speech and thoughts to be an epitome of civilized behavior because he is a lout, but in his very uncouth style he has said it all. This rustic and uncouth manner seems quite appropriate in these circumstances.

Esher Singh has lost his manhood but he feels the beginning of a new sense within him. On the other hand Kalwant Kaur's mind and heart is fixated with only one thought – the woman who in her opinion had captured Esher Singh's passion and she demands to know "Who is that bitch?" The author writes: "Esher Singh's eyes misted up. Momentarily they brightened up and he said to Kalwant Kaur "Do not abuse that bitch."

In these few words does the writer not sum up the entire sentiments of Esher Singh? He stops Kalwant Kaur from abusing the woman but does not hesitate to call the woman a bitch. The direction of this abuse is towards his own self, although it would appear that he is sympathizing with the woman whom Kalwant Kaur has called a bitch. In reality he is seeking mercy for his own state.

If we read on the meaning becomes obvious. Kalwant Kaur roars: "I ask of you who is she?" Esher Singh in a muffled voice replies: "I'll tell you," and he puts his hand to his throat and wipes the fresh blood off, smiles and says: "Mother begotten man is a strange thing."

We see Esher Singh here in a philosophic mood albeit a very basic one. Behind this raw philosophy we observe only one thing. The dead ice cold body of a girl with whom Esher Singh wanted to have hot blooded sex. He smiles not for the sake of smiling but because his smile reflects his awe. As he cannot understand what has happened to him, he smiles to be rid of his anguish and says: "Mother begotten man is a strange thing." This is a big tragedy that can afflict any person. How can it have anything to do with an exhibition of his sexual prowess? How can a story, in which the sexuality of a physically strong and healthy man is rendered impotent, arouse sexual feelings in its readers?

There is no doubt that "THANDA GOSHT" contains certain words and sentences which if detached from their context would seem indecent and uncivilized, but they are an important part of the story as without the use of which the story would remain incomplete. Any word or phrase has to be looked at in the light of its surroundings. If you pick up a piece from a jigsaw puzzle and call it "a donkey's tail" it would be obvious that you are not forming a correct conclusion. Why? Because the piece will have to be put in the correct slot and the jigsaw puzzle looked at as a whole, and it is possible that this piece when attached to the others may become part of a mink stole wrapped around a beautiful woman's neck.

Additionally, we also have to look at what type of a person is uttering the indecent and uncivil words. Esher Singh is an illiterate, uncouth individual whom we cannot expect to speak in a decent language. So, let us now revert to the abuses used in the dialogues spoken by Esher Singh.

We cannot deny the fact that a considerable number of men and women, civilized and uncivilized, make use of abuses in their daily conversation. Esher Singh makes use of abuses in his speech without inhibition because his purpose is not to abuse anyone but because these are catch phrases employed by him in his normal discourse. For example, "And I, sister begat, have killed six people." It is obvious that the use of abuse is neither directed towards his self nor the six people that he had

butchered. "My, mother begat, throat is slit." Clearly the throat
has no mother whom he is seen to abuse. "This daughter begat
has no brain." Again the brain has no daughter whom he could
abuse. Similarly, Kalwant Kaur utters at one place "Is this a
mother begat answer."

At two places Esher Singh says "mother begat man is a
strange thing" and "daughter begat man is a strange thing." As the
defense witness Mr. I. Lateef said: "The use of abuse has
psychological importance." A focused reading of the short Story
can make the reader understand that these abuses reflect the
agony of the perplexed and inquisitive mind and heart of Esher
Singh. He wants to understand his state properly, but is defeated
in the purpose and has to use the phrases "mother begat man is a
strange thing," and "daughter begat man is a strange thing."

July 10th finally arrived. I was extremely anxious and
everyone at home was praying for success. The Judge had
announced four hours for arguments considering it to be a special
case. I was apprehensive of Mr. Inayat Ullah, as I expected him to
be as prejudiced as Mr. A.M.Saeed, and if it turned out to be so it
would have become extremely difficult to control myself. There
were many times in Mian Saeed's Court when such occasions had
arisen but I am amazed as to how I controlled myself.

When we all presented ourselves to the court on the
appointed morning, Mr. Inayat Ullah Khan, in a soft spoken
tone, addressed Shaikh Khurshid Sahib and said "Please excuse
me for about half an hour while I settle these smallish matters."

We came out of the Court room. Arif Abdul Mateen and
Shaikh Khurshid Sahib were both silent. The latter had brought

a number of voluminous law books with him and was probably preoccupied with how and when to cite the references therein. I was only thinking of going to the High Court. Naseer Anwar sat on the grass mumbling a song.

Forty five minutes later we were summoned and entered the court room exchanging salutations with the Judge. Inayat Ullah Khan acknowledged our greetings with a slight nod of the head. When we moved towards the Prisoners dock, the Judge stopped us and directed us, in that soft spoken manner of his, to take the chairs instead. I thought he was addressing someone else but when I looked at him again I realized that the words were addressed to us. We were taken aback, but readily sat on the chairs. A smile was playing on the lips of Naseer Anwar and he appeared quite satisfied.

Before the arguments could start the Judge Sahib said: "I have studied this case very carefully. You gentlemen may remain calm. You will have no problem. From the case file I have only read the decision of the subordinate court and not the testimony of the witnesses as I did not consider it important. However, I have also read the short story "THANDA GOSHT" very intently."

The arguments were about to commence when Mr. Inayat Ullah Khan drew the attention of the prosecution and defence counsels to certain points and asked for clarifications. Shaikh Khurshid Sahib remained generally silent only expressing concurrence with the Judge a couple of times. The Prosecutor's offerings were being challenged by Khan Sahib himself. After nearly half an hour of legal wrangling he smilingly said: "If I were to sentence Saadat Hassan Manto then he is going to say that a bearded man sentenced him." Thereafter he said a few things about the decision of the subordinate court. Eventually he addressed us: "Have you people deposited the fine?" We answered in the affirmative. The Judge then said: "You are free to go. The fine you have paid shall be refunded to you in its entirety." For a few moments I was in a state of shock until Shaikh Khurshid Sahib shook me by the shoulders and said: "Get up people. You are free to go."

When I came out of the court room I gifted rupees ten each to several peons of the Court.

I finally realized that I was actually free and that this fourth trial had also ended on a happy note for me. I thanked the Lord in my heart for liberating me from this great nuisance. Shaikh Khurshid was extremely happy and quite rightly so.

The decision of Mr. Inayat Ullah Khan is as follows:

APPEAL AGAINST ORDER OF A.M. SAEED, MAGISTRATE CLASS – 1, LAHORE

Dated: January 16, 1950

UNDER SECTION 292 PPC

SENTENCE: Arif Abdul Mateen, Fine of Rupees three hundred or 21 days rigorous imprisonment in lieu thereof; Saadat Hassan Manto, three months rigorous imprisonment and fine of Rupees three hundred or 21 days additional rigorous imprisonment if fine not paid; Naseer Anwar, Fine of Rupees three hundred or 21 days rigorous imprisonment in lieu thereof.

DECISION: This Appeal has been filed by three young people, namely, Arif Abdul Mateen, Naseer Anwar and Saadat Hassan Manto. The first two named are respectively the Editor and Publisher of an Urdu Magazine titled "JAVED." The third is a litterateur who, in the special issue dated March 1949 of the said magazine, submitted for publication a short story titled "THANDA GOSHT", authored by him.

On January 16, 1950, they were by order of Mian A.M.Saeed, Magistrate Class One, Lahore, held guilty in contravention of section 292 PPC (Sale of Obscene books etc.). The author, Mr. Manto, was sentenced to three months rigorous imprisonment and fine of Rupees three hundred or 21 days additional rigorous imprisonment, if fine not paid. The other two, that is the Editor and the Publisher, were fined Rupees three hundred or 21 days rigorous imprisonment in lieu thereof, if not paid.

The three have appeared in appeal. The grounds of the decision are included as part of appeal.

The attention of the Government was drawn towards the Story by an officer of the Press Branch and the Chief Secretary ordered legal prosecution.

I have heard the learned counsel of both the parties and examined the file. In my opinion the charge on the accused has not been established and the sentence cannot be upheld. I am of the view that the allegation against the Short Story under discussion that it is obscene and against the law is not correct.

The accused admit their connection with the magazine. The only question that remains to be decided is whether the story is obscene and in particular against the law or not. In this context several issues arise. Firstly, what do we understand from the word 'obscene?' Secondly, is it such an affair wherein expert testimony can be called for? Thirdly, can the under discussion Short Story be held obscene according to the societal standards in vogue?

I have reviewed the Tan Lal etc. commentary in the Criminal Law, Edition 1945, and pondered over the arguments presented by the parties to questions raised therein. The standard of adjudging something 'obscene' laid out therein is: do writings charged as obscene intend to affect minds conducive to immoral behavior, further deprave them and induce and incite them to indulge in indecent behavior? Could such type of writings lead to a moral degradation in the people at large if made available to them? If assessed, that on reading them they would create sufficient cause in their minds to behave badly and in a depraved manner, then the publication of that particular writing shall be deemed obscene. The law seeks to reject such publications. If any writing actually sets out to cause the minds of young persons of either sex or those of older age to be inundated with immoral and sexually provocative ideas then such writing is against the law. This is so, notwithstanding whatever hidden objective the accused, or a laudable innocent, may have, as long as it is anything that incites sexual emotions then it is obscene.

There are numerous decisions which lay down that phrases and sentences shall not be overlooked if the rest of the publication is objectionable, regardless of whether the printed material has been written by a particular author, or written in such manner that it cannot be understood by every one, or that it is of a medical nature and is to be sold to specified customers. We not only have to consider the nature of the writing in its entirety but also the current condition of the environment. If the writing is freely available in the market we are not concerned with establishing whether the buyers are specified or have the right to exercise a freedom of choice. We only have to establish whether such writing can reach the public at large, which includes people of all sexes and ages. Thus we have to examine the nature of the writing in the light of the state of present day society.

I am of the view that that we should leave this matter here and revert to it later after examining whether the issue can be cleared up in the light of expert opinion.

In my view this matter cannot be resolved by expert opinion. We do not have to focus on what opinion some selected and well known writers have formed about the writing. On the contrary we have to examine what reaction the writing will have on the reading public at large.

If I am correct in this thinking then no part of the testimony of witnesses as recorded by the honorable subordinate court is acceptable from this point of view. If, for arguments sake, we were not to attach any importance to the stature of any of the experts and read their testimonies as ordinary testimony, none of the recorded testimonies actually helps the court in arriving at a decision. One lot of the witnesses regards the under discussion article exceptionally obscene and the other contradicts this point of view and declares it a piece of art with nothing indecent in it.

On reflection one observes that difference in opinion is but natural. Different segments of readers react differently. Unless we decide on an evaluation criterion, which is kept in mind, no consensus of opinion can be arrived at. And it is also clear that people having differing temperaments, ages, occupations and type of education will also have differing perspectives about the same thing. Besides this, it is accepted that mannerisms (of characters) are an additional issue. On the question of 'obscenity' there are bound to be differing opinions and perceptions and the divergence could be quite glaring.

In my opinion it would be correct to look at the fictional character in this issue from the perspective of a member of the general public. After deciding this we will have to carry out a focused reading of the under discussion article to determine how far it goes against the accepted societal norms of behavior.

At this stage I would like to refer to an incorrect hypothesis that is also misleading and is an integral part of the under appeal decision. The Magistrate's decision opens with a statement that the term 'obscenity' is related to the particular environment wherein it is decided upon. Different nations and societies have different standards. Up to this point the Magistrate was correct but he erred when he understood that the prevailing standards of morality in Pakistan can only be derived correctly from koranic scriptures. He then says that indecency and sexuality is satanic.

There is no doubt that this is our guidance. But that is not at issue here. It is rather the prevailing state of our society. As is evident we have so far failed to achieve our objectives. Those in appeal must be judged accordingly, that is, what kind of a society we are and not what we ought to be.

When we look around and see the variety of publications that are available in the market which have not been subjected to any kind of regulation, then we can question if the story under discussion is not as objectionable as these. There are no restrictions on "ASRARI" publications which are the epitome of vulgarity. The cinemas exhibit films on which there is no censorship and which as compared to the under discussion story are equally if not more objectionable. If we are to adopt and appreciate the western culture, as we are engaged in doing, then in my opinion the writing that is present before us, ordinarily speaking, cannot be criticized to be obscene. This is a definite result of this culture and no more than that.

Kissing, hugging and embracing are acts that are daily watched in cinemas. Depravity is that common and basic ground on which true stories and never to be forgotten situations are based. In reality this is the basic plot of all English and Western novels. If there is no objection to these then I do not see any reason why we should deal with these young men so harshly.

The under discussion short story appeared on pages 88 to 93 of the magazine. The story revolves around an individual named Esher who has an illicit relationship with a female named Kalwant Kaur. He, during the recent pillage, kills six individuals in a house and kidnaps a beautiful girl from there. He desires to rape the girl, but discovers that the girl is dead. She is "ICE COLD MEAT." According to the story this revelation has such an effect on Esher Singh that he becomes impotent and when he goes to Kalwant Kaur thereafter he is in no condition to meet her sexual demands, even though he puts up an act.

In the Story there is a spattering of some objectionable terms and indecent words as well as some lewd abuses – the kind generally used quite freely by the lowest class of our society. Now to understand the intent of any essay a person would have to keep a large number of such terms in view. For instance, an essay could be in 'good' or 'bad' taste, improper or common or indecent or obscene. To attempt to separate some colors from a prismatic collage for the purpose of declaring an essay obscene is absolutely 'indecent,' 'uncivil,' 'dangerous' and a lot of other things. The most that I can say about this story is that it is commonplace and indecent.

The learned PPS has not pointed out any particularly objectionable paragraphs that could with certainty be declared obscene. Some person has marked some lines but these cannot be held to be any more than what I have already stated and to repeat them will not serve any purpose. I therefore disagree with the honorable subordinate court but this does not mean that I concur with the story. I do not consider it to be obscene or objectionable.

Accordingly, I uphold the appeal and exonerate the three appellants of charges. They are already on bail. If the cash fines have been paid these should be returned to them in full."

Let me share an amusing incident with you. On the morning of July 11th Nazir Ahmed Choudhry, owner "NAYA IDARA" and Editor "SAVERA", arrived. He along with other Progressives had declared me a reactionary and taken an oath to the effect that none of my writings shall be printed in

"SAVEERA". He embraced me and warmly congratulated me. He then said "Manto Sahib, now please handover "THANDA GOSHT" so that I can include it in the book 'Godliness of Nimrod'."

I do not want to comment on this request of Choudhry Sahib.

A few days ago I received a letter from a certain Officer Cadet Mazhar Ali Khan in Kohat. He wrote: "I trust you will remember me. I had met you a few times in the shop of Riaz Sahib and those few meetings were enough to turn me into an ardent fan of yours. Some days back I had read in the papers that you have been exonerated in the matter relating to "THANDA GOSHT." Because of lack of free time I could not write a congratulatory note to you. Anyway even though it is quite delayed please accept my heartiest congratulations. I am quite sure that despite such opposition, fans of your writing are bound to increase.

I have heard that Choudhry Mohammed Hussain Sahib, who used to have lively running battles with you, is no longer alive. Matters will now get rather dull. But the world is full of mad hats. Somebody will soon take his place."

I am really grieved at the death of Choudhry Mohammed Hussain Sahib. May God bless his departed soul. Now that he is no longer in this world I do not desire to say anything about him. Some one will surely take his place and I will say:

Sir-e- doostan salamat ke tou khanjar azmai

(Head of a friend is available for use of your dagger)

Lahore, 29 August, 1950

WHY DO I WRITE

Why do I write? This is as good a question as Why do I eat? Or, Why do I drink? But the first question is different from the others because to eat and drink I have to spend money. And when I write I do not have to spend anything in the form of cash. But when I get to the depth of things I find that this is incorrect, since it is only because of money that I write. If I do not get anything to eat and drink then obviously my mental faculties shall not be such that I would be able to hold a pen in my hand even. It is quite possible that in this state of hunger my thinking process keeps working but it is necessary that the hand also moves. If the hand does not move at least the tongue should work. What a great tragedy it is that a human cannot do anything without eating and drinking!

People place art on an elevated pedestal. They connect it to the seventh heaven. But is it not a fact that this revered and splendid thing is absolutely dependant on a piece of stale bread? I write because I have to say something. I write because I must earn in order to be able to say something. The relationship between the daily bread and art seems apparently strange but what can one do. This is what God has willed. He refers to himself as free of all things. This is wrong. He is neither uncaring nor careless. He asks for prayer and prayer is a very delicate and soft piece of bread, in fact it is like a buttered piece of bread with which he fills his appetite.

Saadat Hassan Manto writes not because he is as prolific a story writer or poet as God, but only because it is God's will that makes him write.

MANTO

Much has been written and said about Manto. Little is said in his favour but more against him. If all these writings are kept in view then it is impossible for a sensible person to form a correct opinion of Manto. I have sat down to write this essay and find it quite a difficult task to express my own views about Manto. But then it could be an easy chore, as I have had the honour of being very near to him and honestly I reckon I am his clone.

Whatever has been written about this man so far I have no objection to it but I firmly believe that whatever has been presented in these various articles is beyond the realm of reality. Some have called him 'The Devil', some a 'Bald Angel.' But wait, let me check whether that hapless character is eavesdropping or not. No, no it is fine, I have just remembered that this is the time when he imbibes. He is in the habit of drinking that foul tasting beverage after six in the evening.

We were born at the same time and will probably also die together. But it is quite possible that Saadat Hassan will die but not Manto, and this has always been a bother for me. This is why I have taken lots of trouble to ensure a continuing friendship. But if he stays alive and I die then it would be like the shell of the egg remaining intact but without the egg white or the yolk in it.

I do not want to get into a long introduction. All I want to say quite bluntly is that I have never seen a more 'one-two' person than Manto in my life. If we were to add up then he would become a three. He has sufficient knowledge of triangles but I know that he has not been tripled. These indicators are such that may only be understood by the knowing readers.

Though I know Manto from the time of his birth, because we were both born at the same time on May 11,1912, he has always tried to remain a tortoise which once it hides its head and neck in its shell is extremely difficult to find. But then after all I am a replica of him and I have managed to study closely every facet of his life.

Now I will tell you how this ass became a Short Story Writer. Critics write very elaborate essays to prove their knowledge. Comparisons are made to Schopenhauer, Freud, Hegel, Nietzsche and Marx. But all of them are many a mile away from fact and reality.

Manto's short story writing is the result of a clash of two opposing influences. His father, may God bless his soul, was a very strict and austere being whilst his mother an extremely soft hearted and gentle person. You can well imagine how difficult it would have been for this bit of grain to emerge from between these two millstones. I now come to his school life. He was very intelligent and extremely naughty. In those days he could not have been more than four feet tall. He was his father's youngest child. He had the love and affection of his parents but had never met his three elder brothers who were much older than him and were receiving education in England. Perhaps the reason was that they were half-brothers. He wanted them to meet him and treat him as elder brothers treat younger ones. But this only happened after the world of Literature had recognized him as a prominent short story writer.

Now please listen about his story writing. He is a fraud of the first order. The first story that he wrote was titled "TAMASHA" based on the blood wrenched tragedy of Jallianwala Bagh. He did not have it published under his own name. This is how he managed to evade the police.

Thereafter, he with his whimsical temperament, decided to seek more education. It should be interesting to note that he could pass the entrance exam only on his third attempt and that too in the third division. You will also be amazed to know that he had failed in the Urdu paper.

Now people call him one of the bigwigs of Urdu literature. I laugh at this because he still does not know Urdu literature. He runs after the words just like a butterfly catcher who cannot catch the butterflies. This is the reason why there are no beautiful words in his writings. He is a basher. But the amount of butts he has received on his neck are happily tolerated by him.

His bashing is not the like the fighting amongst Jats. He lives dangerously. He is the type of person who rather than travelling a clean and straight road only likes to move on a path full of holes. People wait for him to fall but so far he has not done so. Maybe he will fall flat on his face one day and not ever get up again. But I know that even on his death bed he will say that he only fell to rid himself of the sorrow of depression.

I have already stated that Manto is a fraud of the first order. Further evidence of this lies in the fact that he often says that he does not think of a story, rather, the story thinks of him. That too is a fraud. Because I know that when he wants to write a story then his condition is no better than a hen who wants to lay an egg. But he does not want to lay the egg out of everyone's sight. He has to write with everybody around him. His friends sit around him, his three daughters run around making lots of noise and there he squats on his exclusive chair laying eggs which soon turn into stories. His wife is most annoyed with him and often asks him to give up short story writing and open up a shop. But the shop that is open in Manto's head holds a lot more than all the inventory of a grocery shop. This is why he often thinks that if he were to open a store it may well turn into a cold storage where all his thoughts and ideas would freeze.

I am writing this article but I fear that Manto will get angry with me. I can tolerate everything of and about him except his anger. When angry he turns devilish but only for a few minutes. But may God have mercy on one for those few moments.

He does act difficult when writing or when asked to write a story. Because I am his image, I know that he is indulging in a fraud. He once wrote that he has many stories in his pockets whereas the truth lies in the opposite. When he wants to write a story he will think about it the whole night. He will not be able to think any thing through. Five or six o'clock in the morning he will start looking through the newspapers to pick out material for his short story but again without any luck. He will then go to the bathroom where he will attempt to cool down his confused head so that he may finally be able to think properly. But he will fail again. Thereafter in a frustrated state he will unnecessarily start an argument with his wife which he will lose. He will then go out to buy a betel leaf. The betel leaf will keep lying on his table but the title of his story will still not materialize in his head. Then in an angry mood he will pick up a pen or pencil in his hand, write 786 on top of the piece of paper and scribble whatever sentence came first to his mind thus beginning the short story.

Baboo Gopi Nath, Toba Tek Singh, Hataak, Mummy, Mozelle all of these short stories have been penned in this fraudulent manner. It is rather strange that a lot of people consider him to be irreligious and an obscene person. In my opinion he does somewhat fall into these descriptions. This is why most of the time that he writes, the themes turn out to be such that they are considered filthy and the words employed in his writings can be subject to objections. But I know that whenever he starts to write, the top of the first page will always carry the inscription 786 which stands for Bismillah (In the name of God).

This person who often appears to be a non-believer suddenly, on paper, turns full of piety. But he is a paper Manto, just like the papery almonds that can be broken with fingers, otherwise he is a man you cannot breakdown even with a sledge hammer.

I now turn to Manto's personality which can be summed up in a very few words – he is a thief – he is a liar- he is a con artist but he certainly is also a crowd puller. He has many a times, making use of his wife's carelessness, robbed her of hundreds of rupees. He gives her the money and then keeps an eye on where she hides it. The very next day one of the green notes disappear. When she discovers her loss the servants are given a scolding.

Ordinarily Manto is known to be an honest person. But I disagree with this. He is a liar of the first order. In the beginning his lies went unnoticed at home but only because there was a special Manto touch to the charade. But later his wife caught on to him and now knows that whatever is said to her as a special matter is a total lie. Manto only lies for the sake of expediency but the problem is that his family now reckons that whatever he says is just a lie. Just like the artificial beauty spot marked on a woman's cheek with a kohl pencil.

He is illiterate because he has never studied Marx. No book of Freud has ever been looked at by him. Hegel is only known to him by name as is Havelock Ellis. But the interesting thing is people, actually what I mean is critics, assume that he is influenced by all of these thinkers. As far as I know Manto is never influenced by anyone else's thought. He reckons that those counseling him are idiots. The world should not make one understand, on the contrary, one should try and understand the world.

In attempting to understand his own self over and over again he has now turned it into such an understanding that it is beyond and above all thought. At times he indulges in such nonsensical discourse that it makes me laugh.

I can say this to you with absolute surety that Manto, against whom a number of cases for obscenity were tried, is a very clean man. And nothing can also stop me from saying that he is a person who is constantly engaged in correcting and improving himself.

THE FIFTH TRIAL

I had started writing an essay for an issue of "NAQOOSH" but was unable to complete it because I was very ill. I am still not well and I think I am forever going to remain ill. Some friends say that this illness of mine is because of my essay and short story writing.

Tufail Sahib, who is the editor and owner of this magazine even penned an essay about me titled "Manto Sahib." My friend, Ahmed Nadeem Qasmi, who unfortunately has been appointed as the acting editor of "Imroze," wrote a critique on this essay using a pseudonym 'Critic', which is as follows:

"The essay by Mohammed Tufail titled 'Manto Sahib' relates to personal and to a great extent private matters which always remain in the background and should continue to do so. These matters relate to the professional relationship that Tufail Sahib and Manto Sahib have with one another. If the relationship of a Publisher and a writer or an Editor and a writer were to be made public then there will be no rest for either the Publisher or the writer. Every one has weaknesses and faults. But to publish them is something that exceeds the limits of decency. It is correct to reveal minor faults of the writer but only because it may highlight the personality of the latter, but never to indulge in such revelations in a way that the person is rendered useless. From a reading of the essay it appears that Tufail Sahib did not have any bad intention. He perhaps in a flow of emotions wrote certain things which he should not have or at the least not written of them in the way they were written."

I had already written a letter to Tufail Sahib before this criticism had been published.

"Brother,

Assalam alaikum,

Last night Safia told me that you had penned an essay in "NAQOOSH." Because of a drink too many I could not read the article properly. On my request and because Safia liked the essay she started reading bits and pieces from it which I certainly did not like. This became the cause for the abuses that I hurled at you and thereafter I went to sleep.

At eight o'clock the next morning when I read your essay I rather enjoyed it. I do not deny whatever you wrote in it. Despite my weaknesses I am very happy that what you wrote had no element of hypocrisy. Whatever I am has been amply described in this essay. There were certain things in it which are a part of me but beyond the emotion of my senses.

Humbly,

Saadat Hassan Manto"

I no longer want to say any more on this matter – What is a fact cannot ever be denied by me – if I do imbibe then why should I deny it – If I have borrowed money from someone then I should not deny that either – If the world thinks badly of me because of this then let it do so. If I kept on thinking about such opinions that the world may have, then, I would not have been an author of more than a hundred short stories. People of wealth and intellect say "It is correct to reveal minor faults of the writer but only because it may highlight the personality of the latter, but not to indulge in such revelation in a way that the person is rendered useless." I do not know if after Tufail Sahib's essay I have been rendered useless or not. This can be decided later. All I have to say about Tufail Sahib's essay is that he did not keep the medicine and treatment of his sick brother firmly away from public eye and thus helped me recall the age old principle of his fore fathers that never even try to be any ones' guarantor. I am saddened by all this. If I knew of this weakness of his I would have never presented myself in the Court. He would have been arrested and when he were, perhaps, looking around for a guarantor I would have reminded him of his forefathers' advice which he had forgotten in his benign kindness. Forego the guarantee and come with me to jail.

You must have gathered by now from the title that this is the detail of the fifth court case against me.

My friend Naseer Anwar and I arrived at the railway station. The tickets had been bought for us by Tufail Sahib. The question was how to get the seats. We had between us a few bottles of beer. But there was no space even for them on the train. I suddenly remembered that a class mate of mine, Yaqub Taufiq, is the Assistant Station Master at Lahore railway station. As was to be, he happened to be on duty at the time. I went and met him and he immediately secured the seats for us. Thus began our journey to Karachi.

The compartment that we had been given the seats in already had one other passenger, a moulvi sahib, who was constantly working on his prayer beads. I thought this chap will become a pain in the neck so one came up with a prank. I called out to Naseer Anwar to open a bottle of beer. He immediately dived under the seat, pulled out a bottle, opened it and handed it over to me. Watching this, the moulvi sahib, still doing the beads, got off at the next station.

I remembered another amusing incident.

At Lahore station a gentleman along with his wife entered our compartment. Both Naseer and I would have tolerated the husband but to accommodate the wife was rather difficult. In fact she would not have tolerated us. So as they entered the compartment, I said to the gentleman: "Look here Sir, we are drunks, and have fifteen bottles of beer between us which we shall drink and then indulge in talking total rot. You look like a decent person and your wife is with you, so it would be best if you found a place in some other compartment." They seemed convinced by my frank observation and quietly went out of the compartment.

Now when I am writing this article, Tufail Sahib informs me that the said gentleman accompanied by his burqa clad wife went straight to the Station Master and lodged a complaint that the compartment in which they had been given seats was occupied by two blackguards. The Station Master expressed surprise and told them that the compartment was occupied by Saadat Hassan Manto, a very honorable person. The gentleman did not agree and insisted that the person himself had told him that he was a drunkard. Anyway the matter was resolved when the couple was provided berths in some other compartment. We too settled in but the journey to Karachi was pathetic. Even the Second Class had so much dirt filtering into it. Only the beer bottles made us survive the ordeal.

I was thinking of staying in a hotel, but the pocket did not permit it. So finally I decided to go and stay with Khwaja Naseeruddin, but only because my wife had insisted that I go and visit her brother. I thought all the godliness on one side and wife's brother on the other. Thus godliness was put aside in favour of the wife's brother.

He is a thorough gentleman and welcomed both of us warmly. God has been kind to him and he has a very good job, reasonable salary and lives in a big apartment. Incidentally the flat next door to his was vacant, so Naseer and I were put up there.

I had no desire to stay in Karachi for too long as after fifteen years in Bombay there was hardly any attraction in Karachi.

The next day we presented ourselves to the Magistrate Sahib. The small office of the Additional District Magistrate was in an ordinary building. I had been through a number of trials in Lahore. I was aware of the custom at the District Courts, a place where respect had no room.

I stood humbly in front of the Magistrate Sahib. He looked at me and enquired: "What do you want?" The mellowness in the Magistrate's voice was strange for me. I replied: "Sir, my name is Saadat Hassan Manto. Today you have summoned me in connection with the charge of Obscenity under Section 292 against my article 'Above, Below and Middle'."

He looked at me intently and said: "Please sit down." I thought this invitation must have been addressed to someone other than me because such is not the custom in the courts of Lahore. I kept standing. When he saw me still standing he again said: "Please take a seat Manto Sahib." I went and sat on a bench near his table.

After a little while he again spoke to me and said: "Why did you not come for so long?" I replied: "I was unwell." The Magistrate said: "You should have sent in a medical certificate." I lied and said: "I was so ill that I could not think of sending over the medical certificate." The Magistrate heard my lie but remained quiet. He then said: "What do you desire?"

I started thinking about what I wanted. In fact what I really wanted was to be exonerated – I repeatedly thought of Tufail Sahib who had stood as my Guarantor and later had to come very early in the morning with two second class railway tickets because of my carelessness.

After some thought I said to the Magistrate: "Please be done with me. I want to go back earliest." He responded: "This work cannot be disposed off so quickly. I have so far not read the article. God willing I shall read it today and tomorrow morning I shall announce the decision."

Naseer Anwar and I thanked him, hired a motor cycle rickshaw and went off to drink beer. I like this rickshaw in Karachi. It goes phut, phut and a distance of hours is covered in minutes. Even the fare is not too much.

The next day we again presented ourselves in the Court. The Magistrate responded to my salutation and requested us to seat ourselves.

I took the seat on the bench. The Magistrate took out a small piece of paper and said: "I have written my decision." He then looked at the Court Reader and inquired: "What date is it today?" The Reader replied: "It is the twenty fifth."

I am slightly deaf. My ears do not hear properly for some time now. I thought I had been awarded a fine of Rupees Twenty Five. So I said to the Magistrate: "Sir, a fine of twenty five rupees." A fine of rupees twenty five meant that I could not appeal against the decision and the sentence would have stayed put.

The Magistrate had probably fined me Rupees Five Hundred, but when he heard me utter "a fine of twenty five rupees," he smiled, picked up his pen and converted the fine into Rupees Twenty Five.

Naseer Anwar immediately took the money out of his pocket, paid the fine and quietly said to me: "You have been let off easily – Forget the Appeal business– How long do you want to be kicked around in the courts – Have you forgotten 'THANDA GOSHT?'"

I remembered the trial of "THANDA GOSHT" and a shiver went through me. I thanked the Almighty that he had given me relief so quickly.

I offered my salutations to the Magistrate and was about to leave when he said to me: "When are you going back?"

I replied, "Perhaps this very day."

The Magistrate said "No – Do not leave today- I want to meet with you."

I wondered as to why he would want to meet me. Anyway I said to him: "I shall stay till tomorrow."

He said "Where can we meet at four o'clock tomorrow?"

I rattled off the names of all the bars that I had visited. But he was a pious sort of a man and it was finally agreed that we meet at the Coffee House.

The time fixed was four o'clock but we got there fifteen minutes late. The Magistrate was already there. After the pleasantries had been exchanged he very gently said to me: "The only reason that I wanted to meet with you was that you should not return under the impression that I am not a fan of yours."

I was taken aback: "If you are my fan then why did you fine me?"

He smilingly said: "I will give an answer to this after one year."

Many months have passed, a few are left. Let us see what does the Magistrate, who appeared to be a determined soul, reveal.

JUNE 7, 1953

MURDER, MURDERER AND THE MURDERED – IN ONE SHOT

Humans – Antagonizing Humans!

Cliques – Persecuting Cliques!

Nations – Ravaging Nations!

Governments – At War with Governments!

The story of 20th century is not dissimilar to that of the 1st century. Human flesh and bones litter the lands as much today as before. Gallows are still erected to wring human necks. Human blood still gets splayed as much as before. Murder and pillage, barbarism and cruelty still afflict human nature. Innumerable saints, messiahs, prophets, sufis and holy men have come and gone but none have succeeded in rooting out the barbarity ingrained in human nature nor have the man-made laws against such atrocities stemmed the rot or the cause thereof. Yet humanity remains ever resilient and as much engrossed in discovery and hope, pain and grief, joy and happiness as it was thousands of years ago. And this remains the biggest tragedy and comedy of human life. Any discordant move or act in this scenario causes great discomfiture. In this drama of life a single mistake by those at the helm can lead to profound upheavals.

When on the evening of October 16, the news of Liaquat Ali Khan's death reached me I was extremely agitated. Everyone is aware of the fact that human life has to end at some point. Dying by an assassin's bullet was perhaps not unexpected in Liaquat's daring existence. But the manner in which it happened and the way the crowd reacted was certainly not in accordance with the inevitable end. I felt totally disarrayed and agitated and declared myself to be so.

The tragedy did not just relate to Rawalpindi or only to the people sitting in the proximity of the dais but each and every citizen of Pakistan. The news of this tragedy was first received in Lahore by an Englishman. In order to verify the fact he repeatedly telephoned the offices of APP. Not receiving a response he called Radio Pakistan Lahore but there was no answer. So, he too went silent.

The APP teleprinter stirred to life at about quarter to six and after typing "Pakistan Prime Minister Liaquat Ali Khan fired on twice in the Public Meeting at Rawalpindi", stopped, and then went on to print that the announcement stood cancelled.

By seven o'clock all those people who had become aware of Liaquats' injury through the APP's cancelled announcement now rushed for its verification or contradiction by the reputable people of Lahore. But even they expressed their ignorance. Suddenly at some minutes past seven Radio Pakistan announced the fateful news that in the Public meeting at Rawalpindi when Khan Liaquat Ali Khan rose to deliver his speech, a person, identified as Said Akbar, fired twice on the Prime Minister. The bullets hit him close to his heart. He was unsuccessfully operated upon in the hospital and succumbed to the fatal injury. It was also announced that the agitated crowd immediately pounced upon the assassin and killed him on the spot.

The grief wrought by Liaquat's death to Pakistan is evident. The consequential sorrow can also be gauged by all. But no one seemed to be thinking of the resultant damage or how an expert assassin sneaked in and placed himself in the front rows. Let us introspectively examine the snippets of news received thus far:

1. The assassin fired two bullets from a very short range.

2. Immediately after the bullets were discharged by the assassin, the policemen on duty nearby fired in the air causing pandemonium in the mammoth gathering which was until then largely unaware of the assassination attempt. Nevertheless the crowd was quickly brought under control. The Deputy Commissioner Rawalpindi imposed Section 144 in the entire City and Cantonment.

3. Khan Liaquat Ali Khan was rushed to a military hospital where he was given blood transfusion.

4. Khan Liaquat Ali Khan on receiving the bullets fell down unconscious.

These were the first few bits of information that reached the Pakistanis. Differing conclusions could be drawn by people on this basis. What I cannot understand is why the police started firing in the air. Generally the Punjab police is well known for not allowing the unnoticed entry of even a waft of air on such occasions, but in this case the murderer was right before their eyes and his arrest certain. Therefore what was the need for the police to disperse a crowd of fifteen to twenty thousand by firing in the air and that too in such manner that considerable effort took place to overpower the murderer.

It was stated that the policemen were standing nearby but surely on such occasions they must stand in close proximity of the known killer and his target. The police fired in the air but failed to apprehend the assassin who was seated very near them.

The crowd went berserk and it became impossible for the police to save the murderer from being murdered. What this really signifies is that it became extremely difficult to provide immediate medical help to the injured Khan Liaquat Ali Khan and it was due to this reason alone that several blood transfusions had to be given to him on arrival at the hospital.

I am not aware of how long he lay in that injured state on the dais. No one has yet shed light on this aspect, nor on the time taken to get him to the hospital.

As the Late Khan Liaquat Ali Khan was the Prime Minister of Pakistan, on whose command every Pakistani was willing to lay their lives down, then he surely merited the right to know how and why he was killed. What measures were taken to ensure his safety and if such measures were taken why did they fail.

The gist of varying information that reached me till the evening of October 17 is:

1- The assassin of the Prime Minister of Pakistan was an Afghan national belonging to the Jidran tribe. Currency notes totaling Rupees two thousand were recovered from his pocket, (Associated Press).

2- The assassin of the Prime Minister has been identified as Said Akbar son of Babrak, an Afghan national belonging to the Saparkhel clan. Some time back he had taken up residence in District Hazara. A sum of Rupees two thousand and forty was retrieved from his person, and further Rupees ten thousand were recovered from the house where he resided in Abbotabad. The recovery of such a large sum of money indicated that the assassin was indeed hired for this specific purpose only. The documents recovered from his possession included a map which shows all important places in North Western Pakistan. Other documents recovered were in the Persian language and are being currently examined.

3- The Afghan Counsel in Peshawar, Sardar Mohammed Qayyum Khan who belongs to the Royal family mysteriously disappeared from Peshawar approximately five hours before the incident. It has since been established that he had crossed the Afghan border, through Khyber Pass, at about two p.m. in the afternoon and remained at the Afghan Passport office till dusk, proceeding to Kabul later in the evening.

4- In connection with the murder of Khan Liaquat Ali Khan the police are searching for a ten year old boy who was working as the assassin's servant and was also staying with him in room number 3 at the Grand Hotel for two to three days.

5- The Frontier Government had apprised the Government of Punjab of its apprehensions about Said Akbar.

How could those demanding to know the truth about the tragic murder be satisfied with such answers. They remained thirsty and their mental anguish intensified. It was indeed an enigma as to why the assassin who possessed Rupees two thousand and forty and had a further ten thousand recovered from his house was hired to carry out this task. I do not desire to go into the details of the murder nor that of the psyche of the murderer but a question does arise that if he had been hired to deliver this objective why did he carry part of the service reward in his pocket to the scene of the murder wherefrom he had no surety of escaping alive. Two further minor issues crop up from this question:

1. Perhaps the killer was hopeful of escaping alive

2. If so were other people present to save him?

If these issues are kept in sight for a moment then the plot to murder assumes new dimensions. One cannot but only perceive that in most likelihood there were a number of people planted around the assassin who deliberately eliminated him the moment he had fired the bullets. But then it also occurs to one that whosoever, an individual or a party, had instigated the assassin to carry out this bloody act why had they involved a number of other persons in this plan. Did this not amount to stupidity?

Why was the news of the disappearance of the Afghan Counsel from Peshawar insinuated to have some possible connection with the murder? Is it not a fact that any Counsel may at any time decide to depart for his country. There cannot be any strict control on his movements. If Afghanistan had a hand in this occurrence then what was the urgency in Sardar Mohammed Qayyum Khan's departure from Peshawar? The security of his life was the responsibility of the Government of Pakistan. Such questions only arise in a person's mind when full details relating to the matter are not available to that person.

The other news item about suspicions of the Frontier Government relating to the assassin being conveyed to the Punjab Government a day before the incident also assumes great importance. If the Government of Punjab had been duly informed of these suspicions what steps were taken by it in this regard. The Punjab police, which is known to arrest even mosquitoes and flies on the smallest pretext, chose to remain silent even after receiving this vital tip-off. Why did the police not put the assassin Said Akbar under constant surveillance?

The police was searching for a ten year old servant, they said. This is ridiculous. What does search mean. The police should have been able to arrest him within no time and all those who were the slightest acquaintances of the killer.

The Daily 'AFAQ' dated October 20th carried a detailed article penned by an eye witness, Mr. Irfani. The following two points raised by him need further thought:

1. The assassin was seated aslant six feet away from Mr. Irfani's left shoulder. The police started firing in the air unexpectedly and abruptly stunning and rendering witless one and all in the process.

2. As soon as Khan Liaquat Ali Khan fell down the first person to reach him was the Deputy Commissioner Pindi, Mr. Hardy.

Was it also not the duty of the Deputy Commissioner Rawalpindi, Mr. Hardy, who leapt up to reach Khan Liaquat Ali Khan, to chase and arrest the assassin who was only six feet away from the former? There were lots of other people who could tend to Khan Liaquat Ali Khan but securing the assassin should have been the primary concern of Mr. Hardy.

The police fired into the air. Why? Who gave this order?

The answers to these and other questions have not been provided so far and no one knows when they may be responded to.

'AFAQ' dated October 21st carried further details provided by Mr. Irfani of which the more important ones are:

1. The pistol used was not an ordinary one or a cheap brand.

2. No one stopped the assassin projecting his hand forward to fire the pistol.

3. The assassin's body carried many bullet wounds.

4. A man seated under the dais was arrested with a revolver.

5. Deputy Commissioner, Mr. Hardy, had been telephonically instructed by someone to ensure that no other person except Liaquat was on the stage.

6. The assassin on leaving Hazara had sent a written note to the police stating "I am going to Pindi. Will stay at Grand Hotel. Please instruct police not to harass me there as was done during my stay in Murree."

7. The pistol used by the assassin to kill Khan Liaquat Ali Khan has not been located by either police or CID.

All these details are so obvious that they do not require a commentary or explanation by either me or anyone else. There are no veils to be removed. The Hazara police knew where their 'Man' was going and where he was to stay. And even if they were not exactly certain of his new lodgings they were absolutely aware of the fact he was departing from Hazara. Why was he, therefore, not tailed by the Hazara secret police? Generally, any and all movements of even the lowliest political worker do not go unnoticed and his existence is made unbearable. But is it not strange that the would-be assassin of such an important personality, having been under suspicion for a long time, is permitted to leave Hazara with the greatest ease. The would-be assassin not only informed the police of his destination but also the correct address of his new abode. He eventually managed to sneak in unnoticed and seat himself six feet away from his target whom he downs with his first bullet.

He reaches Rawalpindi on October 13th and stays at the Grand Hotel till the morning of the 16th. During the period of his stay his person remains enigmatic and all his actions unusual.

Two or three persons came to meet him at the hotel. The assassin referred to them as CID. In the hotel register he described himself as a "CID pensioner". Is it not odd that despite such dubious declarations no one kept him under surveillance and even if they did they were most negligent in doing so. The murderer was murdered. But is it not amazing that the pistol that killed Liaquat simply vanished.

On October 19, Mian Mumtaz Daultana, Chief Minister Punjab, during the course of a speech stated "I am deeply ashamed that this incident took place within my province. But I want to assure you that there was no lacking in the security measures taken by either the Government or the police."

God willing this may be so but the information so far reaching us neither satisfies one nor removes the doubts. Many bullets were extracted from the body of the assassin. What investigation had been conducted in this respect by the Government and the police?

Said Akbar was the killer of Pakistan's most endeared Prime Minister and statesman. He was a cut-throat. He was the perpetrator of a gruesome act for which he should have been punished. But he should have been protected from the wrath of the crowd. Because of the immense loss caused to our country we can, charged with emotions, offer hundreds of thousands justifications, but the fact is that on the evening of October 16th two persons were murdered. One, Khan Liaquat Ali Khan, Prime Minister of Pakistan, and the other, a resident of Hazara called Said Akbar.

The assassin of the late Khan Liaquat Ali Khan was Said Akbar. The police had already pronounced their decision on him. But who was the murderer of Said Akbar? Was it the overwhelming emotions of the crowd against him? Was it his accomplices who wanted to cover up the conspiracy to murder? Or was it the police? It has recently come to light that three bullets were extracted from the assassin's body. It has now been stated that the bullets had come from pistols generally carried by the police. The name of a responsible police officer is being mentioned in this respect. However, I do not want to say anything about this at the moment. Mian Daultana must immediately inform the people of the full facts. There is no doubt that he had expressed his complete satisfaction in the security arrangements made by the police but if the events are contradictory to his statement then he should not allow any further delinquency in the performance of duty.

It is as much the duty and responsibility of both our Government and the police to investigate not only the real truth behind Khan Liaquat Ali Khan's murder but also the killing of Said Akbar. Ignoring political intricacies, if the incident occurring on the afternoon of October 16 is viewed from a legal stand point, keeping the grounds of reality firmly in view and on the yardstick of what is called humanity, we arrive at the conclusion that there is not much difference between the heinous act committed by Said Akbar and that by his killers. All are murderers and liable to punishment as written out in the Criminal Code of Justice of Pakistan. Their bloody paths were separate but ended at the same quadrangle which was replete with human blood.

Said Akbar caused an irreparable loss to Pakistan by assassinating Khan Liaquat Ali Khan. But the murder of Said Akbar by one or more people resulted in not only his own death but the severing of the arm that was leant upon to inflict this massive blow.

PLACE AND DATE: LAHORE, October, 1951

ALL IS WELL

God is very kind, folks – There were the dark ages, a time of complete ignorance, when there existed, all over the place, District Courts, High Courts, Police Stations, Check Posts, Jails overflowing with prisoners, Clubs where members gambled and drank alcohol, dance halls, Cinemas, Art Galleries and all other types of nuisances. Now, of course, by Gods' grace everything is fine. You do not see a single poet or a musician – God's Curse be on this music which, out of the many nuisances is just one, and after all singing is not something that human beings should indulge in.… You pick up a *Tanpura* and start bellowing. What is being sung? Darbari, Kangra, Malkauns, Miyan Ki Todi and a lot of other nonsense. Some one should ask these people to tell us what benefits were bestowed on humanity by singing these raags and raginis. One should indulge in only such work which may help one sort out one's hereafter, earn some blessings and reduce the ordeal of the eternal grave.

God is merciful, folks, because apart from music all other such absurdities have been eradicated, and, God willing, slowly but surely, the nuisance that is called life will also disappear.

I mentioned the Poet. What a strange character this one used to be. Not a thought about God or of the Holy Prophet but only thinking and running after a beloved. Some praise Rehana and some laud Salma. God's Curse, at times their long, silky tresses are admired and at times their rosy cheeks. They imagine insufferable separations from their beloved. How filthy were the thoughts of these persons! Oh Women and aah Women! But now, folks, all is well. Firstly, the number of women has decreased and those that are left are safely ensconced within the four walls of their homes. Ever since this part of earth has been cleansed of the existence of poets, the atmosphere has turned pure, clean and healthy.

I did not tell you but in the last few years that poetry still survived there were some poets who even started writing poetic lines about the workers rather than their beloved. The talk of beloveds' tresses and romantic hesitations was forsaken for the hammer and sickle. But God is merciful folks, and we are rid of these workers too. They wanted to bring about a revolution. Did you hear? They wanted to subvert the Government, the economic system, capitalism and, God forbid, the religion.

Thankfully we, the humans, are finally rid of all such devils' incarnate. The people had been misled. They had started an illegal demand for their rights. Flags in hand they wanted to establish a government of non-believers. Thank the Lord, none of them is now present among our midst and million thanks to the Almighty that we now have the Government of the mullahs and every Thursday we invite them to a feast of Halva (semolina pudding).

You will be amazed to know that in the days of yore, halva had totally disappeared. The poor mullah in their hujras (chambers) in the mosques! May the Almighty shower the beneficence of heavens on them. Each and every strand of their

extremely long and pious beards cried out for the death of the
devilish razor. May God's mercy be on us. Now no one is able to
get even a razor blade, only halva in whatever quantity, wherever
and whenever, after all it is the mullah's religious diet.

God is Kind..... No one now sings the Thumri or the
Dadra. Film music is also dead. Music has been interred so deep
that not even a messiah can resurrect it. What nuisance music
was. People used to say it was an art form. What art? Wherefrom
art? Is this art, that you hear a song and forget about the
problems of life for a while? You hear a ballad and your heart
starts beating faster. You venture into a fantasy world of beauty
and love. God's curse, art can never be so misleading. 'Ghungat
Ka pat Khol,' 'Payal baja chan chan,' 'Babal mora banara chooto
jai,' 'Ratiyan kahain gawayin re'.....Is there any decency in these
words? Thank God such perversity no longer exists. Thank God
that we have the Qawwali! Listen to it and shake your head in
admiration, get in a trance, yell 'Ho Haq!' and earn His blessings.

Painting too was no less an absurdity. Pictures were
painted of nude and semi-nude torsos. The painter used all his
aesthetic sense to create a perception of beauty. But this was
totally evil. Creation is the work only of God, not the ordinary
mortals. Anyway creating the perception of beauty is a big sin.
Thank God we no longer have even a single painter amongst our
midst. Those who were left had their fingers chopped off so that
they could never again partake in this devilish indulgence. The
state today is that you will not observe even one single straight
line in this country. No such person now exists who may look at
the beautiful scene of the setting sun and have the audacity of
transferring it onto a piece of paper or cloth. To be perfectly

honest that horrible aesthetic sense known as the desire for beauty is now exterminated, so why talk of creation of beauty.

Nudes used to be painted. Sculptures of naked women were being carved out. And it did not end there. These were exhibited in big museums. Those who made these were given awards and purses. Yes sir, awards and purses. Scholarships were handed out. Titles were bestowed to appreciate the work of the artist who drew the picture of a naked woman. The Balls... God's curse... what did I say! Excuse me I will just come back.. I just want to go and rinse my mouth.

I gargled but the taste in the mouth still feels bad. Please pardon me for having uttered something filthy. But then you would not have understood the meaning of these words since all dirty and difficult words have been expunged from all dictionaries.

What was I saying....oh yes.... God is very considerate. No museum or art gallery now survives where naked paintings or sculptures that were deemed pieces of art could be seen. All such places were razed immediately and rubble disposed off in the rivers so that no trace remained of them.

This epidemic of nudity was not just limited to paintings and sculpture. Verses and short stories were also affected by it. A particular poem or short story which described the physical relationship of the male and female was considered most successful. What sick thoughts these people had! They never could imagine spiritualistic glories. They could only talk of this World. There are the seven heavens above but no one has talked of them. God is kind. Such hunger no longer survives in the body and if there is God's benevolence on us then soon only the soul shall survive and the bodies of us mortals will disappear. Thank God for little mercies!

Once upon a time hundreds of magazines were published in the name of literature. Every day material that could deprave the character of a reader was published in them. One could not understand what was this strange animal referred to as literature. If it were something that taught etiquette then it would have been fine. But the stories, novels, essays, poetry, ballads that were published as literary works had no lessons for the young in how to have consideration for their elders and neither for the westernized on how to make use of pebbles to maintain personal hygiene. This is a very fine technique which one masters with the passage of time. There was nothing in it to attract people to keep only beards and have whiskers trimmed.

Literature was in incapable hands – the sexual problems of men and women – God's curse be on them. The Psychology of humans! God forbid! It attempted to reach the eternal soul of ours, the ordinary mortals. Tales of beauty and love were woven. Appreciation of gorgeous landscapes was being written out in flowery words – some were singing of the evenings of Oudh and some of the mornings of Benares. The colors of rainbow were being transferred on to paper. Many a reams of paper were being filled with admiration for flowers, Cuckoos, Koels and other birds. But, folks, the fact remains that praise and admiration can and must only be for the one who created this world.

God is merciful, we now have neither flowers nor cuckoos – the flowers died and the birds disappeared on their own.

Similarly a lot of other nuisances have vanished from this territory to wherever else they could find room in.

I was telling you about literature. Oh yes, did I not tell you that towards the end of that era of darkness a new genre of literature known as Realistic literature had taken birth. In those times people used to say that Realistic literature is about what we see. Woe betide! Just imagine, if at a particular time you had to, God forbid, sneeze, how did it give one a right to put this tragic incident in writing and then present it to every one in the name of literature. You had to sneeze and you sneezed. Why should one get into the details of this incident. To begin with it is unthinkable that there may be psychological aspects of sneezing. You tell me if there can be any? Everything is preordained by Him and also reverts to Him.

Thank God, there is no trace now left of this so-called literature and these self-damned writers. Now no magazine, journal, treatise – God have mercy on us – in those times those people dared to call their filth ridden papers treatises and themselves journalists..... now you do not even see a newspaper, folks. Yes at times the rulers, if they so desire and if need be, do have a few lines printed for our information. And that is the end.

Only one newspaper is now published by the Government and that too only once or twice a year and only if an urgent need is felt. There is no such thing as news. No such incident is permitted to occur that people may hear of and start discussing. There was a time when idle people would sit for hours in homes and restaurants with elaborate newspapers and debating all kinds of issues. Which political party should be in Government?

Which leader should be given the vote? The arrangements for sanitation and cleanliness in the city are not working. Art Schools should be established. Whether the demand for equal rights for women was correct or not. And God knows what other nonsense.

God is charitable, our world is now cleansed of such stupidities. People now eat and drink, pray to the Almighty and go to sleep. No one bothers about any ones' good or bad.

Folks! I forgot to tell you about Science – this was a step ahead of literature. May God keep us safe from this demon. God's curse be on those who indulged in it. They were desirous of converting this mortal world into a paradise. These God forsaken individuals who call themselves Scientists, in competition with God, claimed to create and invent. They said they would make artificial suns that will light up the world at night. We will get clouds to rain whenever we desire.

Please pay attention. Did this not tantamount to the godliness of nimrod? Cure for a deadly, debilitating disease called cancer is being researched. In other words, they are even attempting to take over the role of the angel of death. There is another chap who sits with a telescope and claims that man will reach the moon. Another mad hatter is trying to produce children in jars and bottles. These idiots have no fear of God left in them. Thank God for the fact that all these scoundrels are no longer alive and among our midst.

Now there is complete calm all round. No upheavals and no untoward happenings. No poet and no painter. Life is passing by without any commotion. How satisfying for ones' heart.

People are born and people die but no one hears about it. From birth to death a silent, clear and clean stream flows. No whirlpools and no bubbles. Along both banks on the cool sand lay humans uncaringly fast asleep and, folks, would you also not desire to sleep in a similar fashion till such time that we all open our eyes on the milky canals of paradise. If we were to look up bunches of grapes would fall into our mouths and we would then again go to sleep.

Where has this newspaper come from? Oh dear, I had fallen asleep. The Government postman must have delivered it. The paper has come after a long while. Let us see what is written in it. Those were bad days, folks, but there was one thing to say for them. I have heard that the writing and printing in the newspapers used to be very beautiful. But what is beauty?..... God help me ....What is this?

Wait, Wait. Are my eyes deceiving me? No I can read very clearly.

The Government is in a dilemma. A man has been arrested in the State. Arrested? Has been arrested? The allegation is that he was wandering all over in the streets and lanes shouting that he can no longer live in a Country where there is only goodness and no devilry. God's curse be on him. The special correspondent has stated that when the accused was presented before the relevant authority he started yelling: "Please invite the Devil to this place forthwith or else I shall go mad." The special correspondent also stated that the accused in his own defence revealed the possession of a couplet of Hazrat Allama Iqbal. The couplet is in the Persian language, but it is not to be found in the anthology of the late Allama's works, even though it was published by the Government —quiet correctly — the accused is certainly trying to hoodwink us.....

What else is written - I will read further — the charge is very serious but the Government is in a great dilemma because it does not know where to file the case as no Law Courts exist. If and when the case is heard and if a sentence is passed against the accused there is no place to lock him up as there are no prisons. But information has been received that the Government is undertaking immediate construction of a lock up, a jail and a Court house. God is merciful, folks, the Government has understood the gravity and sensitivity of the matter!

A PROFILE OF ISMAT CHUGHTAI

About a year and a half back when I was in Bombay, I received a postcard from some person living in Hyderabad. The post card carried the following message:

"What is the reason that Ismat Chughtai did not marry you? How nice it would have been if, Manto and Ismat, the two persons had been united. But alas Ismat married Shahid and Manto...."

During those very days a conference of the Progressive Writers was in progress at Hyderabad. I did not participate in it but I did read the details about it in a newspaper from Hyderabad in which it was written that a number of girls surrounded Ismat and asked her the question: "Why did you not marry Manto?"

I do not know whether this was a fact or not. But when Ismat Chughtai returned she told my wife that while in Hyderabad a girl had enquired of her: "Is Manto a bachelor?" Ismat said that she sarcastically retorted: "Not at all." The lady who had posed the question was embarrassed and went very quiet.

There can be all kinds of occurrences, but it is quite interesting to note that of all the places in Hindustan, Hyderabad appeared to be the only city where men and women seemed quite worried about Ismat and I not being wedded to one another.

I had never given this matter any thought but have now started thinking about what may have happened if Ismat and I were in reality husband and wife. This "if" is the same kind of if as: had Cleopatra's nose been an eighth of an inch longer then what effect would it have had on the Nile valley? But in this case neither is Ismat a Cleopatra nor Manto an Anthony. What may be surmised is that would such a union, in the least, have had a far reaching impact on the literary genre of short story writing of our times? The novelettes would have turned into novels and short stories twisted to become riddles. It is quite possible that all the goodness in the heart of these writers turned into powder or burnt up and ended as ashes. It was also likely that their signatures on the nikahnama may well have been the last example of their writing. But no one can say, with hands on their hearts, whether there would have even been a nikahnama. In all probability both would have written a short story on the nikahnama and signed off on the forehead of the Qazi Sahib as evidence. During the course of their nikah there could be a dialogue that ran somewhat like this:

"Ismat, the forehead of the Qazi Sahib looks like a slate."

"What did you say?"

"What has happened to your hearing?"

"Nothing has happened to my hearing. On the contrary, your throat seems to have gone very dry."

"This is the limit. I said the forehead of Qazi Sahib reminds me of a slate."

"Slates are extremely facile."

"This forehead is not facile."

"Do you even understand the meaning of facile?"

"No."

"You have a facile forehead. Qazi Sahib's forehead is....."

"Very beautiful!"

" It is beautiful."

"You are just teasing me."

"You are teasing me."

" I say you are teasing me."

"No, I am saying you are teasing me."

"You will have to agree that you are teasing me."

" Great. You have already turned into a husband."

"Qazi Sahib I will not wed this woman. If the forehead of your daughter is as smooth as yours then I would rather marry her."

"Qazi Sahib, I am not marrying this imbecile. If you do not already have four wives please marry me. I love your forehead."

Krishan Chander writes in the preface to "CHOTAIN": "In the art of concealing the direction, creating a feeling of awe and anxiety in the reader and then changing all of it into happiness, Manto and Ismat are very close to one another and in the art of Urdu short story writing they have very few rivals."

If both of us had ever thought of getting married to one another instead of creating awe and anxiety in others we would have found ourselves knee deep in it and on sudden realization of this state the awe and anxiety would have turned the happiness into a huge tragedy. How droll is the very thought of an Ismat and Manto nikah and wedding!

Ismat writes:

"In the tiny world of love who knows how many Shaukats, Mahmoods, Abbas', Askaris, Younus' and how many others have been shuffled and scattered like the cards in a pack. Can any one pick the trump from among them? Shaukat's eyes overflowing with very hungry stories, the snake like wriggling limbs of Mahmood, Askari's merciless hands, the black spot on Younus's lower lip, the lost smiles of Abbas and thousands of broad chests, broad foreheads, lustrous hair, muscular legs, strong arms have all got together and interlaced like the unbreakable strings of yarn. I, in a state of despair, look at this heap but cannot make out which string to pull at so that it keeps on coming out and I on its strength soar up, up and above like a kite." (Excerpt from "Chooti Behan" -Younger Sister)

Manto writes:

"I can only understand that to love a woman and to buy parcels of land is one and the same thing for you. So why do you not, instead of romancing, buy one or two squares of land and remain the owner of it for the rest of your life. Only one woman in a lifetime, then why is this world full of so many women?

Why are there so many theatrics in it? Why did God not stop at producing the grain? Listen to me; make good use of this life that has been given to you. You are that kind of a customer who, to get a woman, spends his entire life raising capital, but does not consider it sufficient. I am the kind of buyer who will bargain with many women in his lifetime – you want to indulge in such a romance that on its failure a second rate writer may pen a book about it and which is printed by Narayan Dutt Saigol on yellow paper and sold in Dabbi Bazaar at a price no more than that of waste paper. I want to eat up like a termite all the pages in my book so that no trace is left of them. You desire love in life while I wish for life in love!" (Excerpt from short story "DARD" – Pain)

If Ismat could have found the particular string in that tangled mess of yarn which on being pulled keeps on coming out and she on its strength soars high up in the skies like a kite and if Manto had attained success in eating up, like the ants, even half the pages of his life, then the impressions engraved on the literary scene would not have been as deep as they are. She would have stayed up above in the skies and his well wishers would have stuffed the remaining leaves of Manto's pages of life in his stomach and locked him in a cabinet.

Krishan Chander writes in the preface to "CHOTAIN":

"As soon as Ismat's name is taken the male story writers start convoluting. They feel ashamed and embarrassed. This preface is also the result of an attempt to overcome this embarrassment."

Whatever I am writing about Ismat is certainly not to overcome any embarrassment. This was a debt that I am repaying with a little interest on it.

Which of Ismat's short stories did I read first? I cannot remember. Before writing these lines I scratched my brain a lot but to no avail. I felt as if I had read Ismat's short stories even before they had been put on paper. This is why I did not suffer a seizure. But the first time I saw her I felt extremely disappointed.

Adelphi Chambers, Claire Road, Apartment 17 was the office of the weekly "MUSSAWIR" where Shahid Lateef entered with his wife. It was August 1942. All Congress leaders, including Mahatma Gandhi, had been arrested and there was a fair amount of disturbance in the city. The air was reeking of politics, so for a while the topic of our discussion remained the Independence Movement. We then changed the subject and started talking about short story writing.

A month earlier, when I was employed by All India Radio, Delhi, Ismat Chughtai's "LIHAAF" was published in "ADAB-I- LATEEF". After reading it I distinctly remember saying to Krishan Chander:

"The short story is excellent but the last line is rather profane. If I had been the editor instead of Ahmed Nadeem Qasmi, I would have certainly expunged it."

When we started talking about short stories I said to Ismat: "I liked your short story "LIHAAF" immensely. The selective use of words in expression is a characteristic of your writing. But I am amazed that at the end of the story you have written a rather useless sentence that: "I shall never disclose what I saw in the slight swell of the quilt even if I am paid hundreds of thousands of rupees." Ismat immediately retorted: "What is wrong with this sentence?" I was about to reply to the question when I saw the same expression on Ismat's face that one usually sees on the faces of home bound girls when they hear something unmentionable. I felt rather disappointed, because I wanted to talk to her about all the aspects of "LIHAAF". When she went away I said to my self: "She turns out to be an absolute goddamned woman."

I remember that the very next day after this meeting I wrote to my wife:

"I met Ismat. You will be amazed to know that she turned out to be exactly the same type of a person as yourself. It did spoil the taste in my mouth. But I am sure you will really like her. When I spoke to her of the slight swell in the quilt she looked embarrassed at the thought."

After some while I seriously reflected on this first impression of mine and came to the conclusion that for the sake of ones' art a person must remain within its parameters. Where does the art of Dr. Rashid Jehan stand today? Some of it was trimmed away with her hair and some of it stuffed into the pockets of her trousers. In France, George Sands adopted an artificial existence by shedding the beautiful apparel of femininity. He made the Polish composer Chopin work extremely hard to produce gems in music but his own skill suffocated within himself.

I thought of women fighting in wars alongside men, overcoming mountainous problems, becoming an Ismat Chughtai by writing innumerable short stories but there must come a time when her hands must be painted with henna. Her arms should sometimes or the other resound with the jingle of bangles. I felt sorry for having said to myself at that time: "She turned out to be an absolute goddamned woman."

If Ismat had not been a female then we would not have seen in her anthologies of authored works such mellow short stories like 'BHOL BHALIYAN' (Riddles), 'TIL' (Beauty Spot), 'LIHAAF' (Quilt) and 'GAINDA' (Marigold). These are the different facets of a woman, neat, clean and without artificiality. They are not romances or tragedies used to pierce the hearts of men with arrows. These facets had nothing to do with the vulgar movements of the body. The objective of these spiritualistic indicators was the conscience of the human which goes to sleep in an embrace with the unknown, unfathomed but velvety nature of a woman.

"The color drained from his face. Poor child – perhaps his father died."

"Dust in your mouth. God forbid if it happens."

I embraced the child. 'Crack', the child pulled the trigger of his toy gun.

"You idiot – You want to kill your father."

I snatched the gun.
(RIDDLES)

People who say that she is devoid of understanding and that she is a witch are asses. In these four lines Ismat has reflected the soul of a woman. And these people are still looking at it from a moralistic point of view. Such people with twisted brains should be shot.

"DOOZAKHI" (Condemned to hell) was published in "SAQI." My sister read it and said to me: "Saadat, how audacious is this goddamned Ismat. She has not even overlooked her fat brother. What nonsense has she penned." I replied: "Iqbal, if you promise to write a similar essay on my death, by God, I am ready to die today."

Emperor Shahjehan in memory of his beloved had the Taj Mahal constructed. Ismat in memory of her dear brother wrote "DOOZKHI. " Shahjehan got others to lift heavy stones and sculpt them to build a grand building atop the dead body of his beloved. Ismat with her own hands, using a selection of her inner feelings had put her brother's dead body atop the tree top. Taj appears as an undressed marbleized advertisement of Shahjehan's love but "DOOZKHI" is a sweet and beautiful reflection of Ismat's love. The paradise that exists in this essay is not justified by its title.

When my wife read the essay she said to Ismat: "What profanity have you written?" "Shut up. Dear, where is that ice?" Ismat loves to eat ice, just like children who take the cube in their hands and then start chewing on it. Many a short stories have been written by her while eating ice. The copy in which she writes lies on the bolster in front of her, a fountain pen is held in one hand and an ice cube in the other. The radio is on at full volume but both her hand and mouth are simultaneously at work. She has these fits of writing. She may not write for months but when she is seized then hundreds of written pages flow from her pen. She forgets to eat, drink, bathe or wash. She just lays on her stomach on the charpoy and keeps transferring her thoughts on paper in that wriggly, stilted writing of hers.

The very long novel "Crooked Line" was completed by Ismat in seven or eight sittings.

Krishan Chander says thus on Ismat's speed of writing: "While reading the stories another thought comes to ones mind and that is of a horse race. In other words, speed, movement, fleetness and agility. Not only does the story seem to be running along but even the sentences, metaphors and symbols, voices and characters, feelings and senses seem to be moving ahead in a whirlwind fashion."

Ismat's pen and tongue both are very fast. When she starts writing her mind often races far ahead of the breathless words which lag behind. When she starts talking then words seem to scramble into each other. If she ever ventures into the kitchen to show off it would render the effort useless because she has a very racy temperament. The moment she makes a ball of

kneaded flour she starts thinking of a baked piece of bread. She
may not yet have peeled the potatoes but her thoughts are already
thinking of a cooked curry. And in my view there are times when
she steps into the kitchen, famished, but comes out sated with
only the thought of having had a full meal. But despite this
characteristic of raciness I have seen her tailoring in a very relaxed
and laidback manner the dresses of her daughter. Her pen makes
grammatical mistakes when writing but when stitching the young
one's frocks, the needle in her hand does not waver. Measured
stitches and no question of a gather.

In "Children! Oh Dear" Ismat writes: "What is a home? It
is an entire community. Disease may spread or an epidemic may
strike. The children of the world may die one after the other. But
it dare not affect this place. Anyway the home does turn into a
hospital every year. I have heard that children also die. Die they
may, but who knows."

Some days back in Bombay when her young child Seema
was afflicted with whooping cough Ismat would stay up the
whole night comforting the child. She looked lost most of the
time. Motherliness only emerges after one has become a mother.

Ismat is an extremely obstinate person. She is headstrong,
just like children. Any aspect of life, any law of nature will be
unacceptable in the first instance. Initially she refused to get
married and then when she readied herself for it she declined to
become a wife. When she finally agreed to becoming a wife she
then objected to becoming a mother. She bears difficulties and
goes through ordeals, yet, she remains headstrong. I think this is
one way through which she tries to understand the realities of life

by either facing them or dissecting them. Every action of hers is unique.

The male and female characters of Ismat also reflect this strange headstrongness or negativism. They may be madly in love but continue to express their dislike for one another. They desire to kiss cheeks but will instead prick them with a needle. If they wish to pat the other on the back they will slap it so hard that the other person cries out in pain. This aggressive type of negative romanticism that starts off as a mere game ends as a heart rending situation in Ismat's short stories.

If the conclusion of Ismat is also something similar and if I remain alive to witness it I shall not be taken aback.

I have been meeting Ismat for the last five to six years. Because of the very fiery and tempestuous nature that we both have it was always feared that there may be hundreds of quarrels. But in all these years it is odd that we had only one minor spat.

My wife Safia and I were invited by Shahid and Ismat to their home on the outskirts of Bombay for dinner. Shahid was then employed by Bombay Talkies. After dinner we sat chatting away when Shahid said: "Manto you still make mistakes in the usage of language." Till one thirty the next morning I had not accepted that there were usage mistakes in my writings. Shahid had tired by then but till two o'clock Ismat took up the arguments on behalf of her husband. I still did not agree. While arguing Ismat suddenly used a word, hearing which I immediately opined that the correct word was different. By three o'clock Ismat had not accepted her mistake. My wife had gone off to sleep. Shahid eventually got up, went to the next room and came back with a dictionary. The word was looked up and it was established that the word used by Ismat was not even mentioned in the dictionary whilst the one I had used was indeed there with meaning. Shahid told his wife to accept the fact whereupon a verbal battle started between the husband and wife. This state continued till the cocks started crowing. Ismat eventually threw the dictionary aside and started saying that when she would compile a dictionary she would make it absolutely sure that the word used by her found its rightful place therein.

This argument for the sake of argument finally came to an end. Thereafter we never had a quarrel on anything. In fact we did not allow such an opportunity to arise again. During the course of a discussion when we sensed that we were about to reach a point of conflict the direction of the conversation would be changed by Ismat. I would do exactly the same.

I do like Ismat and she likes me. But if someone were to ask us suddenly "Which qualities of each other do you like best?" I think both Ismat and I shall be rendered speechless for sometime.

Ismat is by no means beautiful but she is charming. The impressions of my first meeting with her are still intact in my heart and mind. She was wearing very ordinary clothes. A white muslin sari, with a tight-fitted bold black striped blouse on a white background, a small purse in her hands and heel-less brown colored sandals. Small, inquisitive but sparkling eyes, covered by a pair of glasses with thick lenses, short and curly hair. I did not fall in love with Ismat but my wife simply adored her. If Safia were to ever mention this fact to Ismat she would retort and say:

"Who are you to fall in love with me? Fathers of girls your age have been enslaved in love for me."

I do know of an elderly litterateur who for a very long time remained madly in love of Ismat. He started his romance through correspondence. Ismat kept baiting him but finally got her back in a manner that sent the poor man into orbit.

Because of fear of a clash Ismat and I used to converse very little. If and when a short story of mine got published, she would read and laud it. When the story "NEELAM" was published she exhibited extreme delight quite exuberantly. "Really, what is this nonsense about making someone a sister? You have stated absolutely correctly that it is an insult for a woman to be called a sister." And I kept thinking. She would call me Manto *Bhai* and I would call her Ismat *Behen*. May God have mercy on both of us.

There is, perhaps, no extraordinary occurrence worth mentioning in the five or six years of our friendship. The two of us were arrested on charges of profanity once. I had already been tried twice before but this was Ismat's first time and she was therefore much irritated. As it happened the arrest turned out to be illegal as the Punjab police had arrested us without a warrant. Ismat was very happy but not for long as she eventually had to appear in the Court at Lahore.

The journey from Bombay to Lahore is a long one. But Shahid and my wife were with us. We managed to create quite a good-hearted rumpus on the way. Safia and Shahid started teasing us with attacks on our profane writings. The trials of incarceration were vividly talked about. Ismat eventually blurted out in anger "They can hang me but I will still say I am the truth."

In this connection we went to Lahore twice. On both occasions the college students came in droves to meet Ismat and myself in the court room. Ismat said to me "Manto *Bhai* please ask Chaudhary Nazir that he should start charging an admission fee. At least we will be able to recover the travel cost."

Twice we went to Lahore and both times the two of us shopped at "KARNAL SHOP." We bought from the shop ten or twelve sandals in various designs. Someone in Bombay asked Ismat: "Did you go to Lahore in connection with some court case?" Ismat responded: "No! We went to purchase shoes."

It was I think about three and a half years ago. The Holi festival was being celebrated. Shahid and I were sitting in the balcony of his house and imbibing. Ismat was instigating my wife: "Safia these people are wasting such a lot of money why should we also not participate in this fun?" They kept turning the matter over in their mind for the next hour or so. Suddenly there was some commotion, Producer Mukherjee, his buxom wife and several other people from the film world had attacked us with various colored powders and liquids. In a few minutes our appearances had become totally indistinguishable. Ismat's attention was finally diverted from the drink and became focused on the various colours. "Come Safia let us throw some colour on these people."

We all trooped out into the bazaar and commenced playing Holi on the road. Blue, yellow, green and black colours were being sprayed all over and at each other. Ismat lead the gang. She got hold of a rather fat Bengali woman and plastered her face with tar. At this juncture I remembered Ismat's brother, Mirza Azeem Baig Chughtai, and she suddenly in a commanding voice said: "Let us go and run riot at Peri Chehra's house."

In those days Peri Chehra Naseem Bano was starring in our film " Chal Chal re Naujawan." Her residence was on the same road quite near to ours. Everyone appreciated Ismat's suggestion and within a few minutes we were inside the house. Naseem as usual was in full make up and wore an exquisite silk georgette sari. She and her husband, Ehsan, both came out when they heard the noise being created by us. Ismat was looking like a demon swathed in colours of various hues. Ismat said to my wife, who could not have looked any better or worse with any more colour, in a flattering tone: " Safia, Naseem is really a beautiful woman." I looked at Naseem and said: "Beautiful indeed but very cold." Ismat's beady little eyes moved behind the colour sprayed glasses and she quietly said: "For excitable minds cold things are very helpful." She then moved forward and in a split second had turned Peri Chehra Naseem's appearance into that of a circus clown.

Ismat and I at times used to think up strange ideas. "Manto Bhai, I now desire to write something about the romance of hens and roosters." Or: "I will join the armed forces and learn to fly a plane."

An adequate amount of comment has been made on Ismat's short story writings. Some in her favour, a lot against. A number of commentaries flatter her no end whilst others seem like leprous stumps. Patras Sahib, who has been encaged by the literary who-alls of Lahore, has finally picked up his pen and written an essay about Ismat. As he is an intelligent man, with a sense of humour and sarcasm, therefore the essay that he has penned is very well thought out and interesting. He writes with reference to the label women: "A well respected and experienced Preface writer (he is probably referring to Salahuddin Sahib) keeps the male and female apart in the flock of authors. With reference to Ismat he has stated that in the context of her gender she has just about achieved the same status in Urdu literature as had once been attained in English Literature by George Eliot. It could thus be concluded as if literature were a tennis tournament in which the males and females play separate matches.

"George Eliot has an unchallenged status but merely taking his name is insufficient. But this is a matter for a separate discussion whether there is a scale or criterion which is not external, exigent or incidental but internal, intrinsic and basic for distinguishing the literature turned out by female writers as opposed to the literature produced by male writers and if yes then what is it? Whatever the answers to these questions there cannot be a justification for distinguishing the writers in accordance with their gender and making them stand in two different queues."

The answer to these questions may not be such to make the writers stand in two different queues on the basis of gender but when attempting to answer people are most likely to think of who posed the question? A man? A woman? Asif by finding out the sex of the questioner, the basic and intrinsic approach to understanding the question will become clear.

For Patras to say "that literature was a tennis tournament in which the males and females play separate matches" is typical of him. A Tennis tournament is certainly not 'adab,' (literature), but neither having separate matches for men and women 'bay adabi' (disrespect). Patras when he lectures in his class does not address the male and female students differently. But when he has to reflect on the mental makeup of a male student or a female student then as an educationist he cannot forget the difference in gender.

The fact that Ismat is a woman comes out very clearly in every aspect of her literary writings. This guides us in understanding and appreciating the strengths and weaknesses of her writings and which Patras Sahib has dealt with in an impartial manner in his essay. We cannot separate the gender of the writer from the writer and there are no means, critical, literary or chemical, to do so.

"Cold sighs and mellow fragrance was intertwined with the colours." (TIL)

"Saturated in sweat these had started smelling like the rotten air of a crematorium." (JAAL)

"Male shirt drenched in nauseous cigarette smoke." (HERO)

"Broke off the small and tiny coriander leaves from the lower shrubs and started sniffing them." (MERA BACHA)

All faculties of Ismat, as need be, work in their proper places and perfectly. Aziz Ahmed Sahib says that sex like a disease is spread all over her sensibilities and has requested her not to give prescriptions for it. Well, writing too is a disease. An apparently healthy person, whose body temperature always remains at ninety eight point five, will wait all his existence with the cold, clean slate of life in his hand.

Aziz Ahmed Sahib writes: "The biggest tragedy of Ismat's heroine is that no man has ever loved her with his heart and neither has she loved a man. Love is such a thing whose relationship with the body is similar to that of electricity and wires. If switched on this love will light up like a thousand lamps, may provide breeze like a fan in the heat of the afternoon, may, like the strength of a thousand genies, move the wheels of life and may at times be used to iron out the tresses and clothes. Ismat Chughtai as a writer is not aware of this kind of love."

Evidently, Aziz Ahmed Sahib is full of regret about this. But the love that he appears to be very familiar with seems to have been prepared under some five year plan and he is now desirous of imposing this on others. To make him happy I shall for a moment assume that the tragedy of Ismat's heroine came about with no man loving her with his heart and nor she loving a man in that way.

Actually Ismat is totally unaware of the kind of love written about by Aziz Ahmed Sahib and it is this very unawareness of hers that is the cause of her literature. It is quite possible that if the wires of her life are connected to the electricity of love and the switch pressed to on another Aziz Ahmed may have been given birth to. However, the writer of 'LAIKEN,'

'TIL,' 'GAINDA,' 'BHOL BHALIAN' and 'JAAL,' Ismat, would have surely died.

The dramas of Ismat are weak as they have many divides in them. When she cuts up the plot into various scenes she does not measure it before using the scissor. She jaggedly tears the material up with her teeth and turns the cloth it into a rag. The world of parties is not the world of Ismat. She remains a total stranger in such happenings. Sex overrides Ismat's nerves. Her childhood was not very satisfactory. Ismat is a past master at the details from behind the veil. Ismat is not concerned with the Society but the personalities. Not with personalities but with persons. The only technique known to Ismat to account for the human body is sexuality. There is no direction in her short stories. Her extraordinary power of observation is awesome. Ismat is a writer of obscenity. Light sarcasm, wit and humour are a prominent part of her style. Ismat walks on the edge of a sword.

A lot has been and will continue to be said about Ismat. Some will like her some will not. But more important than people's likes or dislikes is the creative genius of Ismat. Bad, good, naked or dressed howsoever it should remain intact. Literature has no geographical boundaries and wherever possible it should be saved from being enclosed in diagrams and boxes.

Years back a gentleman with the soul of a dervish in Delhi did something odd. He published a book with a title that read something like "Listen to tales of others from me – Reading of it will be beneficial for you." In it he included a short story each of

Meera, Ismat, Mumtaz Mufti, Prem Chand, Khwaja Mohammed
Shafi and Azeem Baig Chughtai. The preface penned by him was
a pathetic criticism of progressive literature and the effort was
dedicated to his two small children. He then sent a copy each of it
to Ismat and me. Ismat did not like this indecent and crude
action of the dervish. She was livid and wrote to me:

"Manto Bhai, have you seen the book published by
Dervish? Please take him to task and send him a notice, on a
personal basis, asking him to pay up damages of rupees two
hundred each per writing or be ready for a legal writ. Something
must happen. You tell me what should be done! It is amazing
that whosoever desires, rubbishes us into filth and we do not say
anything. It could be fun. This person must really be taken to
task and scoffed at for turning into a flag bearer of obscene
literature! He has printed our short stories only to sell his book.
It is our insult to listen to the harangues of any and all Toms,
Dicks and Harry. Keeping what I have said in view please pen an
essay. You may well ask why don't I write it then the answer is
because you come first!"

When I met Ismat I brought up the matter of her letter
and said: "First of all there is Choudhry Mohammed Hussain
Sahib of Lahore who, if we were to make an application to him,
would certainly undertake legal prosecution of Mr. Dervish."
Ismat smiled and said: "Your suggestion is good but the trouble is
that together with him we too shall be held responsible." I
retorted: "So what? The Court may be a very dull place but

KARNAL SHOP is extremely interesting. We shall take Mr. Dervish there!"

And the dimples in Ismat's cheeks deepened.

SAADAT HASSAN MANTO

KRISHAN CHANDER

Tall, slightly leaning to a side, flat faced, fair, veins protruding from the back of his hands, a prominent Adam's apple, large feet attached to spindly legs, a strange effeminate elegance, an annoyed look on the face, a restless style of speaking, acrid manners and a hurried walk. On meeting Saadat Hassan Manto for the first time such an image is formed. But these images are soon overshadowed by another. Manto's forehead is not only as vast as his brain but also odd. Generally, the foreheads of intelligent people seem to look like the foreheads that Western painters attribute to the devil. In other words, an ample forehead with hair combed to disappear behind the ear lobes. Manto's forehead does not resemble the forehead of Satan. His forehead is oblong just like a cinema screen, narrow at the bottom and wide at the top, with a straight, long, dense crop of hair and eyes reflecting a piercing, dour brilliance. An intelligence that depicts as if Manto has been to and back from the jaws of death. I have never asked Manto about this matter though I have heard that he was once afflicted by tuberculosis or such life taking disease. Anyhow, his very large eyes reflect the pain and anguish that show that he had travelled very far along the path of life and then returned. It is quite possible that there may not have been an illness, perhaps just a heart breaking romance. Devastating romance too is no less than a disease. Whatever it may have been it did not weigh him down. In fact that experience turned him into gold.

Manto is as much a Kashmiri Pundit as Jawaharlal Nehru and Iqbal. His family for long has been settled in Amritsar. His two elder brothers have migrated from Hindustan. One elder brother, who is settled in Kenya, is a barrister and member of their Parliament. I have seen his elder brother who supports a beard as prescribed in Sharia, is pious, upright and prayer observing Muslim. Manto, of course, is all that which his elder brothers are not. He respects his elders but does not love them. His opinions, behaviour and mannerism were so different that Manto left his home at a fairly early age to seek new paths for himself.

Aligarh, Lahore, Bombay and Delhi witnessed differing aspects of Manto: Manto the lover of Russian literature, Manto a patron of Chinese literature, Manto the victim of acridity and disappointments, the unknown Manto, the notorious Manto, Manto the regular goer of dens, bars and night clubs. And not to be forgotten is the image of the home-loving Manto, the adoring Manto, Manto the saviour of friends, the Manto who turned bitterness and tartness into sweetness, the notable Urdu writer, Manto. These cities saw Manto's varying hues and Manto in turn came to know these places thoroughly. Manto permitted himself to melt into the experiences of life like a wax candle. He is the one and only Shankar of Urdu literature who drank the poison of life and then indulged with great frankness in talking about its taste and colours. People cower and cringe with fear, but cannot deny the reality of his experiences or the truthful logic of his discourse on life. If Shankar's throat turned blue due to drinking of poison then Manto also suffered on account of his health. His existence had become dependant on injections. This poison could only be drunk by Manto. If it had been any one else he would have lost his senses. But Manto's brain swallowed this poison just like the dervishes of old who started with opium and ended up taking poison or getting their tongues bitten by venomous snakes.

The liveliness and piquancy of Manto's writings and the use of extremely sarcastic and acerbic language indicated that his philosophy of life had reached the ultimate stages of an existence. Prior to meeting Manto I had read his short stories. The weekly "MUSSAWAR," Bombay, used to print his short stories. These stories were so incisive, penned in strange words and obliquely written out to convince oneself of his genius. I had probably read his short stories "SHOO SHOO," "KHUSHIA" and "DIWALI KAE DIYAA" in the "MUSSAWAR" and written eulogistic notes on them to Manto. In those days Manto used to live in Bombay and was the Editor of the weekly "MUSSAWAR." He was simultaneously engaged in the writing of the story, scenarios and dialogues of the film "KEECHARH." Since Prem Chand, Manto was the first writer who moved from literature to films. Perhaps this would not be completely right to say in respect of Manto, because his prominence as a writer emerged after his days in the world of movies. Perhaps Manto was the first writer who reverted to literature from films and after establishing his popularity as a writer returned to the cinematic world. Every action of his was unique.

After reading the said stories I read his short story titled "LALTAIN," (Lantern), which is about the city of Batot

(Jammu) where Manto probably resided during his days of extreme illness. I perceived most of the story as Manto's biography. In various parts of it and in the last chapter sadness and remorse appears to be a part of a romantic Manto's life. Thereafter it appears that someone may have snatched from Manto's short stories all the softness, sweetness and palatability or else he had literally driven these virtues out of his writings. I feel as if he keeps on doing this under the influence of some pain, some motivation or drive. Out, Out, Out, life is too bitter. There is no room for such niceties in it. It is probably better to get out of it. It would appear from his short stories that he has deliberately expunged these emotions out of them. At times he starts griping like children. Sometimes in a harsh tone and at times in an extremely brusque tone he ridicules all. But no one understands that behind this bitterness, rudeness and sarcasm there lay an ocean of softness, mildness and desire to live. Such desire that is eternal and cannot be wiped out. It cannot be erased despite effort. Manto is eternally hungry. Each short story of his is a cry for love. Do not go by his style. He can keep on saying thousands of times that he does not like mankind, that he could love a mangy, emaciated, flea ridden puppy but not humans. He can say that he does not rely on friendship, affection and good heartedness. He can say that his belief is in alcohol. Progressive thought is utter nonsense. He is not a progressive. He is only Manto and maybe not even that. He says all this in a solicitous fashion, at times to hoodwink you, to deflate you, to ridicule you. He says all this but his eyes depict another tale. His pen says something different and it is our good luck that his pen is not under his control like his tongue. He may try to hide his humaneness, progressiveness and love for humanity behind thousands of veils or innumerable coats of paint in his short stories. But his pen is not in his control and behind each story there is an abundance of love for humanity.

At the time I was trying to put together the first edition of "NAEY ZAWAYA," I requested Manto to partake in the venture and he immediately sent me a story which according to my standards is one of the best short stories in Urdu and it now has achieved the same status in literature as Rajinder Singh Bedi's "KRISHAN" and Hayatullah Ansari's "AAKHRI KOSHISH." Such good pieces may no longer be written in Urdu literature. I have read the Russian classical novel "YAMA" and numerous French stories on the same subject as well as studying the character of "UMRAO JAAN ADA" but I have not found a single character like the character of the heroine in "HATTAK" in any of these stories and novels. Manto has peeled off one by one the layers of a prostitute's life in today's society in such fashion that we see not only the nakedness of the prostitute's body but also that of her soul. It is like a glass pane that one can see through either way. Manto was ruthless and merciless in denuding her of her garb but in the ugliness of this game he created a state of beauty. One does not fall in love with prostitution, nor does one feel deeply for Sogandhi's life but one starts believing in her femininity and innocence, her existence and desire and its motivation. And this is what turns a story into an unforgettable classic of eternal literature.

After "HATTAK" innumerable short stories of Manto were published in various magazines and like a flash of lightning his name was etched in the minds of the educated masses. During that time I was asked to join All India Radio and I left Lahore for

Delhi. Hardly a month had passed in Delhi when I received a letter from Manto saying that he was coming to Delhi and would stay with me. I had found a small house in the "TEES HAZARI" area of Delhi and also had a servant therefore I was not at all concerned by his impending arrival. One day at about six o'clock in the evening whilst I was strolling outside my house a tall, lean, slightly leaning to one side, very fair coloured gentleman with a leather bag tucked under his arm arrived. He looked at me smilingly and the two of us recognised each other.

The newly arrived said "You must be Krishan Chander." I could only say "Manto" in response before we embraced each other.

Manto was wearing a long coat. When we went inside he threw his leather bag on the sofa, took off the long coat and sat himself cross legged on a chair, just like Kanhaya Lall in the role of the pickpocket. I burst out laughing and offered him a cigarette. It was probably a very ordinary brand of cigarettes that I had offered him, because he responded to the offer by saying "God's curse. Is this the brand of cigarette that you smoke? It is amazing how you can smoke this stuff and yet write such good stuff. If you keep on smoking such cigarettes you will only be good enough to become a clerk in some office. Understand, Krishan Chander, M.A? Come now and have this cigarette, 555. And forget the cigarettes that you smoke."

The servant brought in a plate of fresh, hot dumplings. I said to him, "These dumplings have been fried in pure ghee which has come from Punjab." He retorted: "Dumplings fried in ghee! God's curse. My dear sir you are a complete idiot. Who in hell fries dumplings in ghee? This changes the taste of the dumplings. For frying you do not use ghee but "DALDA." Everything fries better in "DALDA." Let my wife come and then I shall entertain you with tasty, crispy dumplings just like the fudge of Bombay. Have you ever been to Bombay?" I said: "This is the first time I have come to Delhi and you are asking of the world beyond it. I have no idea about it." "Let us go to Bombay. Forget this radio nonsense. Come have a drink."

Dipping into his jacket he brought out a bottle. It was Solan Whisky No.1. He uncorked it and said: "Come on quick. Ask for glasses. It is getting late."

I had until now never ever tasted alcohol, but looking at Manto's face, which was taut and wore an acerbic expression, I decided not to say no lest what wrath might fall on me. I asked for two glasses to be brought. Manto started pouring the alcohol into one glass and asked me which brand did I drink?

I replied: "Brandy or alternatively some nice English Whisky."

Manto in an angry tone said: "What English Whisky? Whisky is not English, it is Scottish. The bloody English cannot even distil whisky, how can they rule Hindustan?"

I recalled an advertisement of a Scotch whiskey called Haig and quickly said: "I love Haig."

"Its bull shit." Manto said and added: "Solan Whisky No.1 is the best. It costs less but is better in taste and potency than Haig. In future do not drink Haig only Solan Whisky No.1.Understood!"

I said: "Fine. In future I shall not partake of Haig."

Manto was looking at my glass which was nearly a quarter full and enquired: "Shall I pour more?"

I responded: "No more. But do as you wish. Pour more."

Manto looked at me as if amazed and said: "So you are going to drink a Patiala peg!"

I hurriedly answered in the affirmative. I really had no idea what a Patiala peg was, but by saying yes I was momentarily relieved.

Manto looked at me with a lot of doubt and remarked that perhaps I was a big boozer.

The first drink did me in, so naturally I did not take a second nor did Manto offer me another as he had seen my state. I confessed that this was the first time that I had drunk alcohol. On hearing this Manto went on to explain the advantages of alcohol which according to him were numerous. He advised me not to remain being a pundit as I had to create literature, not to teach children at some school. He said that if I did not witness life, sinned, ventured close to death, tasted grief and sorrow or drank Solan Whisky No.1 how would I possibly be able to write?

He finished the bottle and was definitely tipsy. Now his refrain was: "Why are you Krishan Chander M.A.? Why not only Krishan Chander?" Just to tease me he kept on repeating

"Krishan Chander M.A., Krishan Chander M.A., Krishan Chander M.A."

I reacted by saying: "You tell me who are you? Are you a Minto or a Manntu or a Munnto? What is this Manto? Minto – Manntu – Munnto."

It went on like this for a little while until both of us went to sleep; I on the sofa and he on the chair just as he sat except for the neck which was now thrust between his knees. He slept like that. When I woke up the next morning he was still asleep in that posture. The upended empty bottle lay on the table, the glasses empty and the dumplings stale.

I woke Manto up. On waking he said: "If one could get a bit of a drink now the taste of alcohol will disappear from the tongue. You know this is the best way to rid of the stale taste of alcohol. Understand – get some alcohol. I have thereafter to go to All India Radio."

"Why?" I enquired.

"I have been invited to write a drama for them."

"But last night you were sending me to Bombay to work in films."

"Bombay may go to hell. Stop talking rot and order some whiskey." He opened his leather bag and pulled out a short story of his and handed it to me. "Please read it. I usually do not show my short stories to any one. Not even to my father. I can only show it to you even though you do not write that well. There is a particular thing in it. I believe in it. Understand, Krishan Chander, M.A.!"

We remained together at the Radio for a total of two years. After some time Opinder Nath Ashq also joined us. I was a drama producer. Manto and Ashq both wrote plays and I had to maintain a balance between the two. Both were very good writers and both were extremely egoistic. The result, of course, was that some excellent original radio plays that had not been translated from some foreign language were written. These were superb creations of high intellect and with them modern drama had found a permanent place in Urdu literature. In fact thereafter Opinder Nath reserved his best efforts for writing dramas only.

Those were wonderful times. The three of us would engage in literary discourse and debate, write short stories, dramas and articles. We used to read out these efforts to one another. Bedi joined us after some time as did Ahmed Nadeem Qasmi and N. M. Rashid. This small congregation added a new chapter to Urdu literature. Nadeem versified his epic opera, Bedi paid attention for the first time to play writing and Rashid's "MAVARA" was also published during those days. Devendar Satyarthi in the course of his wanderings also arrived. For the first couple of days he and Manto got on famously, but the bitterness of Manto's temperament got the better of the soft, sweet speaking Sathyarthi. It could not go on like this. Manto in one of his short stories took a dig at Sathyarthi. Satyarthi responded to it in his writing titled "New Gods." Manto was saddened by this. The effect of the short story remained in the air for a couple of days and eventually Manto said: "This New Gods – it's ok – put it away."

I never spoke to him on this subject. Manto often said to me: "I do not appreciate this act of yours – I want to have a fight with you and you always manage to elude it. I do not like this nonsense." I would say: "Is Ashq not enough for you to fight with?"

The battles between Manto and Ashq were most entertaining as they encompassed nearly all issues in the world resulting in the creation of such literary thought and metaphoric expression that one would remain amused the whole day.

Manto possessed an Urdu typewriter on which he wrote all his plays. Manto believed that there was no other better thought inspiring machine in the world than the typewriter. He would insert a blank piece of paper into the typewriter, sit back, and then suddenly start typing. Words in a chain just like pearls in a string would appear on the blank paper and soon out of the machine. Unlike the pen whose nib may have flattened or whose ink may have dried up or the paper which one used was too thin. "For a writer a typing machine is as necessary as a wife for a husband. And then there are these two individuals, Opinder Nath Ashq and Krishan Chander, who insist on using the pen. Dear chaps! How can great literature be created with an eight anna worth of a penholder? You are donkeys, just donkeys!"

I maintained my quiet but two or three days later we saw Ashq Sahib walking in with a brand new Urdu typewriter under his arms. He set the typewriter up right in front of Manto and started playing with the keyboard.

Manto reacted by saying: "What can an Urdu typewriter achieve really? One should also have an English language typewriter. Krishan! Have you seen my English typewriter? You will not find a parallel to it in entire Delhi. I will bring and show it to you one of these days."

Ashq on hearing this went out and purchased not only English but also a Hindi typewriter. Now when he often arrived at the Station, the office boy would come walking behind Ashq carrying not one but three typewriters and pass right in front of Manto. Manto only had two typewriters. He became furious and in a fit of rage sold his English typewriter. He was hell bent on disposing off the Urdu typewriter as well but since it was helpful in his work he stopped short of doing so. But not for long could he take to being berated by the sight of the three typewriters. Eventually he sold the Urdu Typewriter and said: "One can claim a lot, but the fact is that a machine is not a match for the pen. The relationship that exists between paper, pen and brain cannot be established with a typewriter. One it makes too much of a noise, whereas the pen flows ever so quietly giving a feeling of the ink flowing directly on to the paper. Ah! how beautiful is this Sheaffer's pen. Just look at its sleek streamlined beauty just like the Christian girls of Bandra."

An embittered Ashq retorted: "Do you have any principles or beliefs? Till yesterday you were full of praise for the typewriter and today for the fountain pen only because I have the typewriters. Brilliant! You have made me expend a thousand rupees!"

Manto started roaring with laughter.

One day Manto came to me extremely happy and said: "Brother, this letter is from Ahmed Nadeem Qasmi. He sends his salutations to you. Please read it."

I read the letter. It was very well written but Manto had given it to me to read only because it contained praise for Manto's short story writing. The praise had forced Manto to share the letter with me. The last sentence of the letter said: "You are the King of short story writing."

After perusing the letter, I opened the drawer of my table and pulled out a letter from it. This letter had also been written by Ahmed Nadeem Qasmi and was received by me that very day only a few minutes before Manto had arrived. I had read the letter and put it in the drawer. Now I showed it to Manto and said: "Here, take this. This letter has also been sent to me by the same gentleman. Please read it."

In my letter Nadeem had praised my story writing skills. The last sentence of the letter said: "You are the Emperor of short story writing."

I said to him: "Manto you are only a King whereas I am an Emperor. I am greater than you. Now what do you say?"

We both started laughing and decided that Nadeem had made a fool of both of us. Manto said: "Let us write a joint letter to him and invite him over."

Educated girls from decent backgrounds, till then, were afraid of taking part in Radio dramas. When I came to Delhi there were only three or four girls that used to take part in our dramas. But when modern drama started portraying households from the middle or upper class families the need to widen this group was felt. Therefore after great effort I managed to create a group of ten or twelve ladies who used to take part in our plays.

One day Manto asked of me how many females could I gather for a radio play. I replied: "What do you mean by how many? As many as you want." He shot back: "Stop bragging! I am asking you." I retorted: "Why do you ask? You write the play and put as many women in it as you want and I shall collect them for it." Manto responded: "Alright I will now write a play which will have a lot of girls in it, twenty six or seven maybe." I reacted and said: "And do title it 'A Man'."

The drama was duly written. It was also broadcast. For each character a suitable female was made available.

This competitive spirit was maintained in all matters. If I penned a good short story so did Manto and Ashq. Rashid would write a beautiful verse. If Manto wrote a play, Ashq would follow suit and I too would attempt to emulate them. All the radio plays including "SARAI KA BAHIR" are products of the days that Manto and I lived together. Those times were so good that despite monetary problems we used to remain very happy, write a lot and whatever we wrote was written enthusiastically and intelligently and not with a wilted heart. In those days Manto wrote the best plays and short stories of his literary existence. There was a tremendous flow in his pen and every second or third day he would come up with something new, a drama or a short story. Despite regular heated arguments and spats there was so much togetherness between the three of us that we spent days and nights together working out ways to further enhance the quality of the programmes. Radio artistes had a great liking for Manto. Manto came to the rehearsals infrequently but when he did he was full of wise cracks and jokes to share thus bringing an air of freshness which lasted for hours. The dramas of Manto were presented by the artistes with such dedication and gusto that they became extremely popular with the public at large. One can gauge the impact created by the artistes by remembering the fact that one of the books of Manto's plays was dedicated by him to these artistes.

During this period Manto and I jointly wrote a film story. For me this was a first venture into the film world. It was entitled "BANJARA." He sold it to some Distributor in Delhi, as in those days we all wanted new suits to be tailored for us and there was no possibility of any money coming from any publisher for a long time. The interesting part of this film story was certainly not the suits but for me at least it was a new experience. The Distributor, a Seth, after listening to the story said: "The story is very good. We will buy it. But Manto Sahib in the film you have depicted the Mill Manager as a very bad person. He should have been shown as a good man as there is always the possibility that the mill labourers would draw a poor inference." Manto immediately said: "We will show him as good." I looked at Manto, awestruck, and was about to say how can this be, when he stopped me with a hand gesture. The Seth again spoke up: "And if this Manager's wife could be shown as his unmarried sister with whom the hero falls in love, just like a vamp. What do you say Manto Sahib?"

Manto remarked: "Very good! Very good, indeed." I was again dumbfounded. This was the same Manto who would not, for any one, change a line or even a word written by him. His short stories were to be published as they were otherwise he would withdraw them. Was this the same Manto? I continued to gape at him.

When we left the Seth's house and came out, Manto said to me: "Dear chap this is not literature. This is a film which is not in the hands of the educated, literary intelligentsia. Our short stories are read by people like Maulana Salahuddin, Kaleemullah, Hamid Ali Khan and others. They are not Saro Bhai Thokarji Patel, or Mungo, Bhango, Jhango and brothers. Therefore in a film to turn a mother into a sister, sister into a beloved and the beloved into a vamp is no big deal for us. Understand? Serve literature and earn money from films. Now tell me do you want the new suit or not?" I retorted: "I certainly do!" Manto shot back: "Then the story for the film will have to be changed." I said: "It shall most certainly be changed!"

From a stand point of temperament, physique, and soul Manto is still a Kashmiri Pundit. There are a lot of commonalities between him and Ashq. I know he will be annoyed when he reads this but it is also a fact that Ashq is a Brahmin. He is a Pundit too. Both are tall and slim. Both are, on a daily basis, worried about the next medical injection. Both reflect the audacity, obstinacy, intelligence and poor temperament of a Brahmin. Both talk a lot. In Manto's discourse there is a greater element of joviality and creativeness. You can talk to him on any subject in this world. He will always offer a new perspective and slant on it. He now avoids walking on the well travelled path and this is now part of his temperament. He cannot give it up. If one lauds Dostoevsky, he will start extolling Somerset Maugham. If you enumerate the pluses of Bombay city he shall immediately launch into an endless eulogy on Amritsar. If you appear convinced of the greatness of Jinnah or Gandhi, he will start talking about the greatness of the cobbler in his locality. If you show a preference for spinach and meat, he will list the advantages of eating lentils. If you desire marriage, he will advocate bachelorhood. If one showed preference for bachelorhood, he will convince you of the advantages of marriage and force you to agree to marriage. If you expressed gratitude for his kindness he would scorn at you. If one abused him, he would start looking for a five hundred rupee job for you. Like Manto's temperament, his friendship, enmity and its revenge are also strange because there is always a reflection of humanity in it. His dourness, frankness and acridity are like some kind of a shell which he wears atop his extremely soft nature. The desire to present himself as different from his friends is nothing more than the fact that in reality he is just like us from within. In fact he is more broken and sentimental and kind than a lot of us. Most people have only seen Manto laughing, drinking and taking a jibe or two at friends or sarcastically ridiculing accepted norms and facts. But I have seen Manto weeping. He does not cry at the sorrows of this world or his own grief. He does not fall in love. He does not face a life-taking illness. He weeps at the death of his first born, year and a half old, child.

As soon as I received the news, I rushed to his house. Manto stared at me with his blood shot eyes as if complaining that I had come too late and only after the child had died and when they were taking him for burial. Where were you before? If you had come earlier maybe the child would not have died. He was hoarse and his eyelids swollen. He said to me: "Krishan! I am not afraid of death. I am not impressed by any ones' death. But this child? I am not saying this because it was my child but only because as you see him he still looks so innocent, fresh and sweet. I think that when a new thought is wrenched away before reaching its logical end a huge tragedy takes place. For me every new child is like a new thought. So, why did it break? I have seen his short life. I may die, you may die, old, grown up and middle aged may die. They keep on dying. But this infant! Nature should not have broken this new thought so quickly." And then he went into an uncontrollable spasm of weeping. The dejected shell of his personality stood shattered in million pieces.

Thereafter I never saw him crying but those tears swept me deep inside that unfathomable ocean wherefrom Manto's creative thinking emerges. The colour of this deep Ocean is dark green and golden. Its water is brinish and there in its depths, whales and octopuses and other dangerous mammals lurk, but down there can also be found colourful coral reefs on whose velvety green rest beautiful conch pearls. I had witnessed this strange scene only once. Have you seen the pearls that Manto, the deep sea diver, keeps on bringing out from the depths of his heart? These actually are dried up droplets of his blood which are glazed in his sarcastic and incursive style and presented in a thought-provoking manner to us. Do not go by his style. These are real pearls. It is the misfortune of our country that we do not respect them. To wit, Hindustan is always referred to as the cradle of civilization, literature, art and culture but for eons we have forsaken our great craftsmen and now we seem to not even realise the intensity of our crime. Saigol comes to mind. When he died there was not a single soul from amongst the great personalities of our country who uttered a word of sympathy. And these are all those people who go hoarse talking all the time of the continued survival of arts, crafts, tradition and culture. But if someone were to ask them who the great craftsmen, literati, writers, painters, singers and artistes of Hindustan were and what they were doing these days, these people will become speechless and offer their extremely busy life as an excuse to remain silent.

Manto has no liking for good clothes but has preference for a nice home, good food and drink. You will always find his house in immaculate order. He is used to working in a clean, neat, righteous environment. Cleanliness, discipline and excellence are the hallmarks of his character. He has no room for carelessness and shoddiness that one often witnesses in the homes of writers. At Manto's home you will not find anything that is not aligned. Only the thoughts of the Lord of the Manor are askew. Skewed indeed but even there one discovers a systematic arrangement which is generally revealed at the end of his short stories. Manto's short stories are a reflection of his temperament and environment. Manto prepares the apparel of his stories very diligently. One cannot see any folds or pleats or any use of weak threading. His linkages are strong. Well thought out, faultless short stories in non-convoluted, plain and simple language. Yes, the colours of his stories are odd. They are honed in an exquisite manner with a unique use of metaphors. The stories do not possess the traits of juiciness, verse or superficiality. He does not believe in beauty but a geometrical logic in literature. He keeps everything measured. He is well acquainted with the meaning, effect and parameters of his metaphors. He does not rely on a senseless use of beauty but moves methodically and in geometrically shaped patterns to create a situation and is often more successful than most romanticists. Manto stays close to the ground, so close that very often even the features of the crawling insects on a shard of grass are seen crystal clear. All those who are used to looking at life in a casual, superficial manner fail to appreciate Manto's depth of observation and perception. There is no doubt that at times his enlarged ego dupes him, or he fails in maintaining, between life and literature, a balance as between the insects in the grass and the floating clouds in the sky and adopts a very personalised and anarchistic approach. But this happens rarely and most of his creations measure up to the best standards of humaneness, simplicity and honesty. Their bitterness incorporates such sweet beauty which the human heart seeks every day.

In the early stages there was a dominant influence of Russian writings on Manto. This is not strange. Not only most of the Progressive writers in the world but even those who were reactionaries in their thoughts took advantage of the legacy of Russian literature. But after a short time Manto developed his own style of writing which belongs only to him. Superb imitators of the writing style of Abbas, Ashq, Ismat and Krishan Chander abound but to date no one has been able to copy the writing style of Manto and to some extent that of Bedi. In Urdu literature there is only one Manto and one Bedi. You will find somewhere or the other reflections of the remaining writers. In particular the bold and blatant manner adopted by Manto in his writings on expressing the problems of sexuality is not to be seen in Urdu or Hindi literature or for that matter in any translations from Maharathi, Gujarati and Bengali languages that I have read. To find similarity in other languages is difficult. Manto first exposed modesty and then the shell of prudishness. He goes on to wipe off the layers of filth and only then picks up the now cleansed and glowing theme to highlight the importance of sex and its intricate and widespread implications in such manner that everyone has now become abundantly aware of. For this sex education we are indebted to Manto.

This education he provided to us by sacrificing both his youth and health. The lanes of Bombay, the bars of Bombay, the night clubs and houses of ill repute of Bombay – Manto had made an introspective study of the world of criminals. In search of truth he found himself mired knee deep in filth. His clothes must have been dirtied but his soul was never tarnished. The sadness hidden in his short stories is a witness to this. He is more convinced than any one else of a woman's honour, virtuosity and homeliness. Therefore if he sees a woman losing her honour or virtue or home, he takes it personally. He becomes restless and turbulent and desires to know why it was so happening. Why? And when each time he brings forth his own experience to look at this continuing system, arrangement and societal order, he, in great anger wants to thrash himself. Manto does not believe in appealing. He believes in scaring and thrashing. There is a slap at the end of each of his short stories that hits the face of every reader with such force that the reader cries out and starts abusing Manto. But Manto does not refrain from this beating. He never will. A lot of critics refer to this as Manto's sadism. But this is not sadism at all. It is in fact a changed appearance of his injured humaneness. This very attribute is to be found all over in Manto's talk and behaviour, his creations, his deeds and words.

There are a lot of things in Manto's life that cannot be talked about during his lifetime and therefore neither be written about. Despite that I cannot restrain myself from writing this one anecdote.

This incident took place when I was employed at Shalimar Pictures in Poona. I had gone to Bombay to take part in the Progressive Writers Conference. I inadvertently bumped into Manto in a local train. We were together for about ten to fifteen minutes. After some small talk Manto suddenly asked me: "Brother, I had sent a female to Poona to meet with Mr. 'S,' it was her desire to become an actress. What happened to her?" I replied: "That girl is with Mr. 'P' these days." I then enquired of him: "You must have studied her?" Manto in a serious tone said: "God's curse. I only study prostitutes. I never go near a decent girl."

This was Manto's typical style. Then hesitatingly he said: "The poor girl appeared extremely decent to me. But this stomach! It is a very bad thing." He then remained silent for a long time while I felt the extent of modesty, shame and virtuosity in that man. He always desired to see a woman neat and clean, pious and virtuous. And when anyone wants to see life, creativity and beauty bereft of dirt, filth and pollution then there can be no doubt about the person's healthy outlook towards life. His literary integrity would have to be believed in. His standards of morality would have to be accepted. At least I am completely convinced of this. It is a different thing when Manto just for the sake of annoying me may pen a story or two to contradict my philosophy. He can do this. But this reaction is not representative of his skill, image or literary capability. His prominent skills and capability lie in human beauty, humaneness and a desire to improve the lot of humanity.

And these attributes are the deep footprints of his literature.

TO MANTO

AHMED NADEEM QASMI

Dear Saadat!

When I heard the news about the forthcoming launch of the bi-monthly "URDU ADAB" as well as the fact that you and Mohammed Hassan Askari are part of the Editorial Board I managed to disappoint a number of people by remarking that: "There is nothing wrong in it." On being pressed to explain my remarks further, I said: "Amongst all living short story writers in Urdu Manto's technical and personal capability is most prominent. His personality cannot be embedded into any other and his literary skills so real and incisive that in order to digest the same all of Mohammed Hassan Askari's available knowledge and experience would have to stealthily make use of his modernist thinking."

A few of the objectors concurred with me while the remaining decided to defer the matter till the publication of the first issue of "URDU ADAB." In reality I believe that this togetherness of fire and water is a good omen for new literature and, I, who am convinced of the genius of Mohammed Hassan Askari, whose criticism reflects the style of Firaq and Abdul Ghaffar, will in your company, with that blatant plain speaking of yours and the extreme uniqueness of your literary viewpoints, will impress upon him a writers' literary and social position and cause him to desist from insulting, ridiculing and labeling them as communists and start taking them seriously and sincerely. I have expressed this belief many a times in front of a number of literary personalities and this is why I also submitted a poem for "URDU ADAB."

On August 01, 1948, you wrote to sister Hajra (Masroor). In the letter you had requested her to forward some of her writings for "URDU ADAB." This letter also bore the signature of Mohammed Hassan Askari. I started reading that letter with great interest because I expected that it may include a declaration of the editorial policy of "URDU ADAB." I had placed a bet with sister Hajra. She was saying that the thoughts of Mohammed Hassan Askari were like a sugar coated quinine pill and even such a strong personality like Manto's would be duped by it. I did not agree with her but after reading only the first line, "This Magazine does not follow any particular School of thought," I realized that I had lost the bet. My sister was not happy to win the bet, in fact, she very sadly uttered: "This is Askari Sahib speaking." I in an unsure manner replied: "Perhaps Manto will say something later on, in such manner and in such words that they will suppress the voice of Askari."

I kept on reading the letter but slowly my loud voice turned into a whisper. When I had finished the letter, I felt as if I had suffered a big intellectual defeat. As a person I have great respect for you and that is not to say that I do not view you as an ordinary writer of passable caliber. Perhaps you are one of the first writers whose life and art reflects homogeneity. I sat quietly, in utter silence for quite some time and started wishfully thinking that only if you were not a signatory to this letter. I wished you would have refused to sign or forgotten to sign. I wished that your individualism may not have been so unknowingly crushed. I wished that you may have thought that instead of a restorative injection you had signed on a prescription of sleeping pills. Manto, whose name is to live for centuries, appears to have retreated, while Askari, (I wish he had never studied the French language), whose intellect is adrift in the deserts of limitless study, has risen in such glory that in the process not only Manto's presence has become blurred but also distorted.

I am not saddened by the fact that you have declared modern literature as an "ism" and called it a "mere din." I am saddened by the fact that in the 1944 Annual issue of "ADAB-E-LATEEF" (which had been compiled by me) an article of yours entitled "Modern Literature" had been printed, wherein you had written: "The time will come when the exact meaning of modern literature will become apparent." You had not used the term modern literature as a common place expression but something which was a part of you. You wrote: "Some people refer to modern literature also known as new literature, in other words, progressive literature, as Saadat Hassan Manto and those who dislike the harsh masculine gender call it Ismat Chughtai."

In that very essay you had announced that you will not let this "ism" die. In fact you had advised people to first put an end to that environment and those conditions that had forced them to adopt the "ism." "Those people who desire an end to Modern literature, Progressive literature, and obscene literature or call it by whatever name, must take the correct path and exterminate the conditions which give rise to such writing."

What I want to ask you is have those conditions been eradicated by the Baudelaire and Flaubert provoked philosophy of Hassan Askari? Has, as per yourself, "The dense divide that exists between men and women" been pulled down? That very wall whose layers of plaster were vowed to be scrapped off by Ismat Chughtai's sharp nails? Has the rampant filth of the cities been removed from the beautiful valley of Kashmir? Seeing which "Poor Krishan Chander would weep softly, softly"? Have those weaknesses of humans in general and Saadat Hassan Manto in particular been gotten rid off that you had telescopically observed yourself and promised to remove in full public view? If all of these problems have been eliminated then you may happily say good bye to Progressive writing. But if the dense partition between males and females has become higher and thicker, if in our villages the heaps of filth have turned into mounds and if the air is permeated with a noxious smell then, my dear, the "ism" is still alive and the duty of Ismat, Krishan and Manto has not ended and your signatures on the statement penned by Mohammed Hassan Askari do not look good.

I have always called you a Mussalman. Nor am I a communist. I am not even a regular member of the Progressive Writers Association. The ingress of the Indian army on Kashmir is considered an act of aggression by me. Sajjad Zaheer declares that the Progressive Writers Association includes writers of all thoughts but has termed Faiz Ahmed Faiz and myself as belonging to the League. I am a patriot of my country. Pakistan is my veins and blood but I cannot agree with the literary thoughts of Mohammed Hassan Askari because the literature that he wants to project is, in my opinion, going to be the murderer of the evolution of Pakistani people. Perhaps you have not seriously deliberated on the fact that he is bent upon making literature the fiefdom of that particular class which in Marxist terminology is referred to as bourgeoisie and generally as the middle class. To succeed in this dangerous venture he has adopted such a course that causes ordinary masses to be taken aback on reading any reference to religion while the higher classes smilingly see in the depths of this cry for religion an enhancement of their personal interests. Mohammed Hassan Askari assumes that by taking this route he is performing a great service for the masses or that he has thus crowned himself as a literary reformist.

I claim that there is no other bigger conspiracy than this effort to keep the minds of Pakistanis embroiled in a state of confusion and discontinuance. Mohammed Hassan Askari complains that Progressive writers do not even acknowledge the existence of a Muslim nation as in their enthusiasm for the humanity at large they want to see India and Pakistan once again united under the feet of Nehru and Patel. In this context he generally refers to the writings of Indian authors. Perhaps he does not realize that the Progressive Writers Association of Pakistan is a totally different institution and the connection with the Indian association is only as much as yours or Mohammed Hassan Askari's or mine with any other Progressive Associations of East and West or an Indian friend. The Progressives of India can view the issues of Kashmir, Hyderabad, Junagadh etc., as they may desire, but we cannot be concerned with them, because these are also issues of their country and they are free to view them in the light of their own national interests. We are Pakistanis. Our considerations are different. We think and view our problems in the light only of our own welfare and progress.

You will not find a single example of any Pakistani Progressive
Writer's literary effort reflecting treachery to Pakistan.

So then why does your co-signatory Mohammed Hassan
Askari repeatedly state that Progressive Writers (whom he refers
to as "Writer-folk ala Kipling's monkey-folk" only to suit his own
convenience) are engaged in misleading the Students and Young
men in order to dismember Pakistan? The fact is that Progressive
literature has over shadowed his faculty of criticism. Otherwise
Brother Saadat! Is securing the rights for the ordinary people of
Pakistan, of whom 99% are Muslims, a treachery against
Pakistan? Is it also treachery to condemn the rampant bloodshed
and carnage so that such inhuman acts are brought to a halt? Is it
also treacherous to talk of destroying the feudal and capitalist
institutions? And is it not treachery to lean on the Indian
Progressive Writers to vomit poison about Pakistani Progressive
Writers? Is it not treachery to place before the Pakistani writer
the example of Andreyev and be told that loyalty should not be
with a Country but with a Government? And is it not extreme
treachery to hand over the Government to every new invader and
later sing songs of praise in their favour?

The problem with Mohammed Hassan Askari is that he
laments about the non-existence of a particular thought amongst
the Progressive Writers but then is exasperated when those very
thoughts are expressed in writing. He enquires of the
Progressives as to how much feeling and respect do they carry in
their hearts? In my opinion the following answer to this question
is more than enough: "The foundation of our movement is based
upon the feelings of the masses, adopting those feelings as ones
own and giving them due and total respect." He asks: "How do

you value hopes and aspirations?" The reply is that: "It is this very analysis of their hopes and aspirations that infuriates and inflames you and those at the helm of affairs." The Progressive Writers are not indifferent to their people in the manner of Hassan Askari. They are the true and loyal advocates and well wishers of millions of Pakistani people. They are aware of and acknowledge the fact that their own security and well being is intertwined with that of Pakistan. Hassan Askari, because of this vision that they carry, is now dreaming of throwing their writings to the mice and burning the same.

Furthermore love of mankind is not such a bane that it should cause discomfort to Hassan Askari. Being a Muslim he should be aware of the fact that there is no greater lover of mankind than a Mussalman. Love of mankind does not teach one to be treacherous to ones' own country or people. In fact whenever a writer talks about bringing to an end the economic divide, feudalism, bonded land labour and capitalism and advocates the love of humanity it is Mohammed Hassan Askari, (because it is now a habit with him), and all those whose vested interests lie with these inhuman practices who are taken aback and instead of referring to the writer as a true Muslim they abuse him of being a Socialist. And when Hassan Askari sits down to label the modernists as agents of the Soviet Union then why does he not mention, in addition to Sajjad Zaheer and Ehtesham Hussain, the names of Faiz, Khadija, Hajra, you and me?

But he has in the last few days talked of you very lovingly. In the August 15, 1948, edition of the daily "IMROOZE," (I am sure you must have not only read it but also heard of it), he writes:

"I had no deep interest in the short stories of Manto earlier but now that time has started distinguishing between the genuine and the fake it transpires that amongst the modernist writers Manto is the only person to have any interest in human mind and its condition."

Why now dear chap? Before now when you considered Urdu short story to be a waste of time it was the same Manto whose compilations were being sold yesterday, as they are today, right upto August 15, 1948. So far no new collection of his short stories has appeared. Yet suddenly you have found a deep interest in Manto? Have you ever asked Hassan Askari this question?

I am sure you have not posed the question. Now there is no need to do so. I will give you the answer. When suddenly from the mountain of a critic a eulogistic fountain of Manto's literary prowess has erupted, the only reason for this is that Mohammed Hassan Askari needs you now for the vital task of creating fissures within the ranks of modernist writers.

Why is he so anxious to create this division? There is no other reason for it except the fact that before partition of the sub-continent his political views were quite different from the Communist writers and till to date he continues to tread the same track. A discourse on differing political viewpoints is extremely useful. But can there be any meaning to the dragging of literature into purely political or personal differences? By indulging in this Mohammed Hassan Askari is giving rise to an air of animosity against Pakistan and to cause disarray within the ranks of Pakistani writers. He does vociferously shout "unity, unity" but this very slogan was also raised by Hitler, as well as

British imperialism, American capitalism and the Russian democracy. Unity of thought and action is a most effective tactic but here the situation is that the slogan of Unity is being raised in the "IMROOZE" while in the "SAQI" reunification is being talked of in such subtle manner that no one can raise a finger. I implore you to think about this and feel about it. I know you are a very sensitive person, dear chap!

Another matter that requires special attention is that to instigate a gagging of the progressive writers, Mohammed Hassan Askari has written aplenty in the "NIZAM" and other papers and magazines. Dr. Hijazi of the "Civil and Military Gazette" also adopted the same approach. When their wishes bore fruit resulting in the closure for six month each of "NAQOOSH," "SAVERA" and "ADAB-E- LATEEF", the first person to protest against this move of the Government in the daily "PAKISTAN TIMES" was no other than Mohammed Hassan Askari! Had all the poetry, short stories and essays that appeared to have caused serious misgivings in his mind and minds of similar ilk, been published in unknown, fringe rags? Certainly not, the objective only was to cause the closure of these prominent and well read magazines and having succeeded in doing so these people suddenly rose vociferously in support of the magazines. This uproar too was the result of well thought scheming.

This appears to be the right time to expose the desire for recognition of the literary ambitions of Hassan Askari. This is what is called opportunism. This is how one can control the thoughts of easily influenced, innocent minded writers. This is what is referred to as stabbing in the back. And Brother Saadat, if

"KHOL DO" had not become moot at this juncture then Hassan Askari would have continued his untiring appreciation of the Government's actions. The benefits that he may have derived from the situation evaporated because Manto was an accused. Somebody should ask Askari Sahib what were the compulsions that made him write the sentence: "The Nation would have to deal with literature and writers the same way as Fifth Columnists are dealt with." Now that they have been dealt with in that manner why have you raised your banner in their support? Now you may sit in solitude and smile and try proving from the perspective of a fascist artisan that what ever has transpired was in good taste.

The fact is that after Partition the number of good, well known writers in our country stood drastically reduced. Amongst the few that are left, you stand very prominent. This reason made Hassan Askari suddenly realize your literary genius and he decided that Manto was a short story writer par excellence. And you in turn somehow suddenly discovered that Hassan Askari is a noted literary critic of Pakistan. I find it amusing that in the middle of this air of mutual lauding and admiration is encamped Urdu literature which the two of you are involved in creating - Manto and Askari – Life and Lethargy – Fire and Water!

Please do not mind, Brother! You had set out to bring Hassan Askari back on the right track, but the artificial flowers in the garden of his craft seem to have overawed you resulting in your moving away from your path. I cannot even imagine that you too were so culpable of being influenced to such an extent by someone else's person. I have nothing against Hassan Askari. In my heart I have respect for the gravity of his thought and literary ability. For four or five years we were in constant communication with each other and in the letters we wrote neither one of us abused the other but in fact carried on a literary discourse. He, after compiling a selection of poems and short stories written by Progressive Writers, decided to Part Company from them. I attribute this to his interest in the French language. He can again come near them and to make him do so is your duty. You, who is seen these days as his friend and admirer, appear most suited to emphasize the fact on him that: "if you had some problems with a few progressive writers before partition why should that feeling be persisted with now. Why do you go after every thing with a big stick in your hand? You considered Firaq as the leading Urdu poet. But if the present state of your 'objections' continues, as is the case, then very soon you will consider the poetry of every poet to be a masterpiece of his 'creative human mind and its state' who joins the ranks of the magazine 'URDU ADAB' or who befriends you." Please try and bring Askari around not with your stories but with your philosophy of life. But if you cannot do this do not try to move away from this movement which is and shall remain eternally proud of your craft and its effects. And if you do not mind my saying this the Progressive Writers Movement has never dealt poorly with you. Hassan Askari proclaims to be in favour of "literature for literatures sake." But in his opinion: "The Pakistani Writer is about to commence on the journey wherein the values and dreams shall be called Pakistan. Give us the stories and poems that you understand and others will also understand. This is the only way in which we can help improve the stability of Pakistan."

This is exactly what literature for life, literature for propaganda and literature for mankind is. If Hassan Askari has written these words with a deep feeling then why does he sit alone, half asleep? This is what modernism is all about. You are a flag bearer of it. But now you reflect an utter dislike for Progressives! You desire to pen only Urdu literature for the sake of Urdu literature. But pure Urdu literature is only going to be representative of the aforesaid thoughts as highlighted by Hassan Askari. This is exactly what is referred to as modernism. Why the duplicity in policy then? Why doesn't Hassan Askari clearly say that he desires to become a literary dictator (in these days of People's Democracy) rather than trumpeting the call of literature for literature's sake as Pakistan building? This in fact is Progressiveness. The fanfare only creates an unbearable noise.

Brother Saadat! I have known you for ten years. I am an admirer of your sincerity and open heartedness. I am neither in denial of your literary capabilities. But as a writer I would like to say to you that please do not get involved with the quibbling of words and the labyrinth of logic. You have in your hand an explosive pen and your brain is full of intense emotions. You can only fruitfully use these emotions and the power of the pen only as long as you continue to have a hold on the pulse and exposition of real life (as you have done so far). Pakistan has great expectations of you. In this age of development please stay away from the opium of literature for literatures sake. Urdu literature must be produced but according to some predetermined thought. Do cooperate with Hassan Askari but only after testing his thoughts on the yardstick of life. Please express your views openly on all those activities of the Progressive Writers Association of Pakistan that you do not subscribe to. Please help the Association in improving itself. Do tell those sitting by the sea coast waiting for the oarsmen to be drowned that at times the massive tides of the sea can engulf the coast as well. Please come closer to us and help the modern thought to prevail as that is what is required for the Stability of Pakistan, Welfare of the Pakistani people, democracy and parity. Please be sure of your exalted standing in the craft of literature. If a critic suddenly becomes aware of your literary capabilities, then, beware, he probably needs you to carry out some deeds. Otherwise, to call the sun a sun does not lead to an enhancement in its intensity!

Your brother,

NADEEM

LAHORE, 15 SEPTEMBER, 1948

BACK DROP

"Have you heard the latest news?"

"Is it about Korea?"

"Certainly not!"

"Is it regarding the Begum of Junagadh?"

"No!"

"Must be some fresh incident of murder or killing?"

"No! About Saadat Hassan Manto."

"Why? Is he dead?"

"Not at all. He was arrested yesterday."

"Must had something to do with obscenity?"

"Yes. The police searched his house too."

"Did they find any cocaine or illicit alcohol?'

"No. It was reported in the newspapers that nothing illicit was found in his house."

"Despite that his very existence is unlawful."

"Yes, at least that is what the government thinks."

"Then why was he not detained?"

"To detain or not is in the hands of government. They can detain or release whoever they desire. And surely this is a matter that should remain in the hands of the government. They know all the intricacies of such matters."

"Then surely he would have been prosecuted for taking his own life."

"I think this is the reason why he did not commit suicide. Otherwise he is not the type who can be stopped from doing his own bidding."

"So what you mean is that he will continue indulging in obscenity"

"Dear chap! This is the fifth case against him. If he wanted to desist he ought to have reformed after the first case against and engaged in something decent."

"For example taking up a government job, selling oil or creating potions like Mr. Ghulam Ahmed of Mohalla Pir Gillanian."

"Oh yes. Opportunities for decent work abound. But he is so obstinate that he will write and only write."

"Do you know what this will result in?"

"Obviously a bad end."

"He will have six cases against him in the Punjab, ten in Sindh, four in the Frontier Province, three in East Pakistan whose pressure he will not be able to withstand and will go mad."

"He has already gone mad twice".

"This was foresight on his part. He was rehearsing so that when he actually does go mad, he will be at ease in the mental asylum."

"What will he do if he does actually go mad?"

"He will attempt to restore sanity to those who are insane."

"That would be a crime."

"Don't know, only a lawyer can tell us, whether the Pakistan Penal Code contains a section against such acts."

"There must be one. Restoring sanity to the insane seems to be a very serious crime under section 292."

"With regard to Section 292 the High Court announcing its decision on 'Thanda Gosht' clearly stated that the law has nothing to do with the motive of the writer, good or bad, the law only takes notice of the intention of the writer."

"That is why I was stating that no matter what the purpose of restoring sanity to mad men, it is important to take notice of the intention behind the act, which cannot be considered innocuous under any circumstances."

"These are legal intricacies and we should stay away from them."

"Thank you for the timely alert- thinking such thoughts itself is a serious crime."

"But, Sir, if Manto actually does go mad what will happen to his wife and children?"

"His wife and children can go to hell - why should the law be concerned about that?"

"Quite right. But will the government not help them?"

"Yes, government. The government is a different matter - I personally think it ought to help them. If nothing else they should at least announce in the newspapers that the matter is under consideration."

"By the time the whole affair is considered it will be forgotten."

"Indeed this is what always happens to such issues."

"Damn Manto, his wife and his children. Please tell me what effect the High Court decision might have on Urdu literature."

"To hell with Urdu literature as well."

"No sir, please do not say this. One's heard that literature is the wealth of nations."

"Maybe. But we only consider cash lying in our banks as wealth."

"Indeed, what you say is absolutely correct. So Momin, Mir, Ahsan, Zouq, Saadi, Hafiz and others of the same ilk will also be taken care of under Section 292?"

"It must be so or else there is no point to it."

"All those who consider themselves writers and poets should come to their senses and adopt some decent profession."

"They should become leaders."

"But only of the Muslim League."

"Yes. This is exactly what I meant. To become a leader of any other League would be simply obscene."

"Totally obscene."

"There are other decent trades apart from being a leader. One might sit outside a post office as a scribe of decently worded letters, indulge in penning advertisements on walls, or become a clerk in the employment office. After all this is a new country and there are many job openings, they can all fit in anywhere."

"Yes there is so much room."

"The government is thinking of creating a new colony near the Ravi for prostitutes and harlots, to clean the city of such filth. Why should not these poets, writers and novelists be made a part of this lot?"

"An excellent idea. All of these people will be most happy together."

"But what will be the outcome of this?"

"Who thinks of the outcome, what will be, will be."

"Yes, they can sit there and twiddle their thumbs. Dog can eat dog and profanity will breed more profanity."

"A most interesting scenario!"

"Manto of course will get a lot of what he enjoys most."

"But the damned chap instead of watching their dances will start writing about them. He will present many a Sugandhi and Sultana."

"Many Khushias, many Dhondhos."

"I do not understand why the damned chap gets so much joy in resurrecting such depraved characters. The whole world finds them hateful but he alone embraces them and loves them."

"His sister, Ismat, was quite correct when she said that Manto loved bizarre and sensational situations which could jolt the sleeping out of their slumber. He thinks that if a number of people are sitting around dressed in white and someone walked in smothered in mud and slime, everyone would be taken aghast. In a crowd of sobbing individuals, a sudden rip-roaring laughter would leave the rest stunned. Such acts he reckons will create a lasting impression."

"His brother Mumtaz Hussain says that when he goes out looking for goodness, he strives to bring it out of a person you least expect. A person who is incapable of doing good. This is Manto's achievement."

"This is not only absurd but most indecent too. How can goodness be brought out of such a despicable person who is nothing but offal and gut."

"And slime-covered rushing into a crowd of decent people."

"This is even more profane."

"Where does he dig up so much filth from?"

"Don't know – he just finds it somewhere or the other."

"He himself is an epitome of filth."

"Let us pray to God that we may be spared his despicable existence. His salvation also lies in this."

"No doubt!"

"O God – God of all humanity – the merciful – the benevolent – we two sinners ruefully submit to you that Saadat Hassan Manto, son of Ghulam Hassan Manto, a most decent, God-fearing and benevolent man, may please be taken away from this world since he disdains fragrance and loves odorous garbage. He does not open his eyes in the haloed light but grovels in total darkness. He is not interested in the clad but the naked among humans. Sweetness holds no attraction for him, but he loves bitterness. He ignores married women but enjoys the company of prostitutes. He relishes filthy pools rather than clean and clear waters. Where weeping is required he prefers to laugh and where laughter is required he cries. He revels in showing us the cleaned-up faces of those blackened by their own misdeeds. He forgets you and runs after Satan, who disobeyed you, dear God.

O God of all humanity, please remove this scandalmonger, this filth-loving pervert from this world. He is only interested in wiping off the grime of the disheveled, the unscrupulous and the immoral. Oh God he is mischief personified - the judgments pronounced by the courts thus far are ample proof of these facts. But then these are man-made courts. You must take him away from this world and bring charges against him in your heavenly court. He should get the punishment he deserves. But please God be on your watch for he is a great charmer and you may just fall for his charms. But you know everything. Our only prayer is that he should no longer live in this world, and if he does he must learn to live like us and cover up the faults of others.

This prayer comes from our hearts for an eternal world."

(28 May 1952)

MY MARRIAGE

I wrote some while back that there had been three major accidents in my life. One was my birth, details of which I remain unaware of, second was my wedding and the third becoming a short story writer. A fourth one is still ongoing therefore to say anything about it would be premature.

Those people who desire an inside view of my life, for their sake only I am going to narrate the tale of my marriage.

I must first describe the background to this accident so that the exact details of it are highlighted. I do not remember the year but it was about twelve or thirteen years ago when I was expelled from the Aligarh University because I was afflicted by tuberculosis. I borrowed some money from my sister and went off to Batot (a small village between Jammu and Kashmir), to recuperate. After staying there for a period of three months when I returned to my city of Amritsar I found out that my sister's son had died. (She had been married to someone from Bombay and after a few days in Amritsar had returned to Bombay).

It is important to disclose here that my father was dead. Whatever money had been left behind by him was handed over to the son-in-law by my very kind hearted and innocent mother. The state of affairs now was that we were penniless and dependant on others. My two elder brothers were giving us Rupees forty a month.

As soon as I returned to Amritsar my heart and mind were very perturbed. I wanted to run away or commit suicide. If I were a strong willed person I would have surely committed suicide. This is why when Mr. Nazir, owner of the weekly "MUSSAWAR," Bombay, wrote to me inviting me to accept the editorial chair I did not hesitate, immediately gathered my luggage and went off to Bombay. I did not give any thought to the fact that my mother will be left all by herself in Amritsar.

Mr. Nazir employed me at Rupees forty a month. When I started sleeping in his office he began deducting rupees two per month as rent. Thereafter when he secured for me a job as "MUNSHI", a clerk also referred to as a dialogue writer, in Imperial Film Company at a salary of rupees forty a month he reduced my salary at the magazine by half and continued to deduct rupees two as house rent.

This was the time when after achieving great heights the Imperial Film Company was in a state of decline. The owner of the company Seth Ardeshir Irani, a spirited person, was extremely busy in trying to restore the condition of the company. In such an uncertain state the employees were not getting paid on time. Seth Ardeshir made a blunder by importing "New Colour Process" machines in order to achieve the making of the first colour movie in India. '

When this colourful burden fell on the company its financial condition worsened. But, the work moved on howsoever. Some advance was received against the salary while the unpaid amounts were added to the ever increasing balance of arrears. As it happened, the responsibility of direction of this movie was entrusted to Mr. Moti B. Godwani, an educated gentleman who liked me. He asked me to write the story, which I did. He appreciated the story but a problem arose. How could the Seth be told that the story of the first colour film had been penned by a petty clerk? After great deal of discussion and thought it was agreed that to receive good money for the story an established name would have to be used.

No such person could be found within my circle of acquaintances. But when I looked further I found far afield in Shanti Naketan Professor Ziauddin (now deceased) who was then a Professor of Persian at Tagore University. The Professor was affectionate towards me, so I wrote him a letter. He very kindly agreed to become a part of this fraud of ours.

The story of the film was attributed to his name but the film flopped which resulted in worsening the condition of the company. During this time on the recommendation of Mr.Nazir I secured a job with Film City at rupees hundred a month. When Mr. Kardar came to Bombay from Calcutta, Film City entered into a contract with him for the making of a film. Stories were sought, one of which was written by me. Mian Kardar liked the story I had written and started work on it. But fate had something else in store.

Seth Ardeshir found out that I was now working with Film City. Although he no longer commanded the status as before, his influence and powerful personality was still respected. He, perhaps, exchanged some harsh words with the owners of

Film City which resulted in my being flung back by the ear to the Imperial Film Company. The story that I had written was also returned.

My salary was increased from Rupees forty to eighty and I was promised a separate compensation for my story. The direction of this story was handed over to Hafiz ji (of Rattan Bai fame).

When I took up employment with Film City I had abandoned the use of the office of "MUSSAWAR" as my residence and set up house in a small room in a filthy building at rupees nine per month. The room was overrun by insects and they fell from the roof of the room like rain drops. My mother had arrived in Bombay and was staying with her daughter. When she came over to that filthy room for the first time to meet me tears filled her eyes.

The relationship between my brother-in-law and I were distraught at the time. May God forgive him but he had a bad character. Because I would criticize him, he had banned my entry into his home. He had also put a stop to my sister meeting me.

I was talking of my mother's tears. Tears that filled her eyes only because her son who had been brought up with great love and care now lived in such a dirty place, had no clothes, used a kerosene lamp to work in the evenings and ate at a restaurant. As long as she kept crying I went through great mental and emotional anguish. Remembering days that had passed by was absurd and weeping and sobbing meaningless to me. I have always been concerned with the present. I never think about the time that had passed or the tomorrow that was to come. What had to happen had happened and what was to occur would also occur.

On being done with her crying my mother in a serious tone enquired of me: "Saadat why do you not earn more?" I replied: "Bibijan what will I do by earning more. Whatever I earn is sufficient for me." She chided me and said: "No. The fact is that you cannot earn more. If you had studied more it would have been different."

She was correct. But my heart was not in studying. Thrice I had failed the entrance exam and when finally I did enter College my meaningless wanderings increased even further and thus I failed the F.A. exam twice. When I went to Aligarh they threw me out because I had tuberculosis. Despite feeling the harshness of these realities I jokingly laughed the matter away by saying: "Bibijan whatever I earn is enough for me. If there were a wife in the house then you would see how I earned. To earn is not a difficult task. A man can acquire lots of money without being highly educated."

On hearing this, my mother suddenly questioned me: "Will you marry?" I replied non-seriously: "Yes! Why not!" Thereupon, she lovingly caressed my head and said: "So, you are to come to Mahim this Sunday. You will stay standing on the footpath, and when I see you I will come down. I will take care of this business of your marriage, God willing. But do come with your hair cut."

I did not have the hair trimmed, but the night before I had polished my canvas shoes. A pair of white trousers, which had been laundered urgently at double rate, was donned and on the morning of the Sunday I was standing on the footpath in Mahim, very near "Angelleto Mansions." My mother was waiting for me on the balcony of a flat on the third floor. When she saw me she came down the stairs and asked me to accompany her.

Twenty or twenty five yards away there was another building – Jaffar House – my mother on reaching a flat on the second floor rapped at its door. A maid servant opened the door and we went in. Mother went to the ladies quarter while I was welcomed by a middle aged, extremely fair man who took me to the male section of the house and seated me there with great love and respect. He immediately opened up and started asking me about my interests and hobbies.

He was a Government employee and worked in the police department as a finger print specialist on a nominal salary. He had many daughters and enjoyed going to the races and playing flush. He used to do the crossword puzzles regularly but had so far not won any prize. I recounted my state of affairs and also told him that I was working for a film company which did not pay a regular salary but occasionally advanced money to keep one alive and kicking. I was amazed that even after I had told him that despite my rather dire financial conditions I also drank a bottle of beer every evening, he did not seem to mind it.

He listened to me very carefully. By the time I was ready to leave Malik Hassan had become aware of all the important aspects of the book of my life.

When my mother and I got out of their apartment, she told me that these people had migrated from Africa. They knew my brothers very well. He had worked as a barrister in East

Africa for ten or twelve years. They had a daughter whom they wanted to be married off. A number of proposals had been received but they had not accepted them. They actually desired a boy from a Kashmiri family. She told me that she had talked to them about me and not withheld any detail. So, if anything was left from the revelations that I had made those gaps had been filled up by my mother!

But now I started thinking about the matter. What if these people agreed to the proposal? I had doubts about this happening because there was nothing in or about me that could have persuaded them to give their daughter's hand in marriage to me. But if it did happen I would actually have to wed her and then try and earn loads of money.

Malik Sahib had invited me the following Sunday to his home to share a meal with him. When I got there he welcomed me very warmly. The meal was served. It included chicken, meat balls and spinach curry as well as a chutney of mint, coriander and dried pomegranate seeds. The food was delicious but overly spiced, peppery and hot. I started sweating but gradually got used to the excessive use of condiments.

I was invited on two or three more Sundays by which time I was now very familiar with them. My mother then broke the news that they had accepted the proposal. When I heard this my head went into a spin. I had only regarded this talk of marriage as a joke. I was absolutely certain that no persons in their sane mind would be prepared to give the hand of their daughter to me. What all did I possess? Only entrance passed and that too in the third division and working at a place where instead of a regular salary only an advance was paid. My profession was films and journalism. Whichever decent person would want to have anything to do with such a person?

In order to secure a filthy room only I know of the efforts that had to be made. The owner of the building had found out that I worked for a film company. It was only after a large number of recommendations to him that he was ready to let the room to me.

I felt extremely agitated and worried. I was not at all ready to accept this news. I lost my mental balance even more when my mother told me that she had already given her word. I did not say anything to her but day in and day out I found myself in deep thought trying to work out how to wriggle out of a self-created dilemma. After considerable self deliberation I arrived at the conclusion that further thought on the matter was totally futile and I should reconcile and like the proverbial boatman plunge my boat into the roaring currents of the unknown river.

Although I had taken the decision but a new problem arose as to where the money required for the 'NIKAH' (nuptials) would come from. This was an extremely worrisome question. The company had now stopped paying even the advances. And then there was mother who had fixed a date for the ceremony. I thought of escaping from Bombay but some unknown force stopped me from doing this. There was now only one way out and that was to go and meet Seth Ardeshir and request him for some money for my 'NIKAH' ceremony. The company owed me nearly rupees one and a half thousand. If I could get all of the money not only all the immediate problems would be over but in fact I would have enough left over to enjoy as well.

I met Ardeshir Sahib. He did not have the time to listen to my tale carefully. He listened to me whilst moving from one place to another. Finally, he said to me: "Look here, you know the state that the company is in these days. If the condition had been better I would have married you off at my own expense." It is true that when the company was doing well he would provide lavish help to his employees. He was very benevolent but nowadays he was in such financial straits that the very thought of not being able to help anyone aggravated him no end.

You can understand my disappointment. When I was about to leave he called me back and said: "All I can do is to buy your essential requirements for you – go and fetch Hafiz ji." I immediately brought Hafiz ji to him. He made him note the addresses of a few shops, wrote something on a chit of paper and said: "Take Munshi Manto with you and buy for him whatever he wants."

I went along with Hafiz ji in a motor car. The first stop was a cloth merchants shop. I bought two saris from there on Seth Ardeshir's personal account. The next stop was a jewellery shop. A person from there accompanied us as I wanted the girl to select the jewellery herself.

The man from the jewellers and I reached Jaffar House. The girl's mother, whom I called aunty, was shown some jewellery by the man. She selected one diamond ring, pearl drops for the ears, a pendant and two gold bangles. I tried to persuade aunty to keep a few more pieces but she did not want to over burden me unnecessarily. I wish I had told her that such an occasion is not very likely to arise again. The company owed me rupees one and a half thousand. Please do not let go of the disappearing opportunity. But alas! I could only recover four or five hundred rupees from it as the company died immediately after my 'NIKAH.'

Nazir Sahib now restored my salary to rupees forty a month. This provided some relief in that I would still be able to afford at least one beer every evening.

The 'NIKAH' proved disastrous for me as not only the remaining money to be recovered from the company was now totally sunk but additionally I had hurt my knee.

Please listen to this tale also. I had no friends or close ones in Bombay except a sister. But I was forbidden to go to her place. All the work had to be done by myself. A few people had to be informed that I was getting married, dried dates and candied cardamom seeds had to be purchased, hair cut was to be had and then to get on a bus to go to the front!

After inviting Syed Fazal Shah, the owner of Shah Jehan Hotel, to the 'NIKAH' ceremony, I slipped on the polished floor of his hotel and fell down so heavily that I lost consciousness.

In my life I have lost consciousness only thrice. First, after extending the invitation to Syed Fazal Shah (deceased) as just mentioned. Second, on my mother's sudden demise. Third, on my son's death. This falling down and losing consciousness was not a good omen. The injury was extremely hurtful, because when after regaining consciousness I attempted to descend the stairs the hurt leg refused to walk. I hobbled to the market in great agony and at each step I cried out.

Anyhow I purchased the dried dates and candied cardamom seeds and reached Mahim. In great agony I climbed the stairs of Jaffar House and arrived at the 'NIKAH' ceremony. There were about fifteen or twenty people there. I sat down against a bolster cushion. I could not bend the injured leg so I let it lie straight, even though this was extreme bad manners. But when Qazi Murkhay (a strange name) asked me to sit cross legged there was no choice despite the pain and agony of the injury.

Once the formality of "Do you" and "I do" was over, I breathed a great sigh of relief. I straightened my injured leg and swallowed many an ache and pain, received congratulations and walked back limping to my home. I lit the kerosene lamp and lay myself on the bed that was full of bed louse and started to convince myself that I had actually got married. I honestly tell you that despite the few dried dates and candied cardamom seeds in my pocket and the knee injury I could not believe that such a momentous event had taken place in my life.

Well I was just about married. The only thing lacking was that my wife was not with me in the rupees nine a month room of mine. According to law I could have asked her to come with me whenever I wanted but I dared not do so. How and where would I feed her? At the Irani restaurant, and that too on credit! Where would I keep her? There was hardly any space in the room for even a single more chair! And, obviously, wives take baths. But there was no attached bath room! The building was double storied and there were forty rooms in it. All the people living in them just had two common bathrooms available for their use and their doors had vanished a long time back. I was feeling extremely agitated on this account. I was now married and sooner rather than later I would have to be living with a girl as husband and wife. I had no prior experience in these matters and had no idea as to what is a wife and what is a husband.

Two or three girls had crossed my life but they were maid servants. I collided with them the same way as two blind persons would while walking on the road and immediately thereafter take their respective different paths. I honestly felt that I could become anything but not a husband. It was not the same as writing essays and short stories.

Time passed by. I made efforts and joined a company called "SAROOJ MOVIE TONE" at rupees one hundred per month. It appeared as if the company was just waiting for me to join. Not even two months had passed when it went bankrupt. I was now convinced that my 'NIKAH' was very unlucky for me.

But the very street smart owner of "SAROOJ MOVIE TONE," Seth Nano Bhai Desai, ensnared a rich Marwari, renamed "SAROOJ MOVIE TONE" as "HINDUSTAN CINE TONE" and was back in business. I wrote my second film story titled "KEECHAR" for the new company which was later produced, premiered under the very odd title of "APNI NAGARIA" and was a success.

The film was hardly fifty percent done when the Marwari Seth lost his entire wealth in silver speculation including his spotless white limousine. I linked this event to my 'NIKAH' as well! I was sure that very soon this new company would also go bankrupt. But Nano Bhai Desai somehow managed to borrow money from here and there and completed the film.

It had been nearly ten months since my 'NIKAH' had taken place that I was involved in an utterly embarrassing incident. I had a friend called Ashiq (lover) who was a complete nincompoop. He was illiterate, uncouth, a sycophant but an expert in dance. To please me, one evening he bought me a beer, drank some himself and started chattering. Whilst ranting on he took me in a car belonging to a friend of his, to a girl who according to him was a student of his. On getting there he knocked at the door. A female voice from within enquired: "Who is it?" Ashiq replied: "Ashiq." The voice within responded with an emphatic abuse "----- Ashiq." He got extremely annoyed and broke the door down and entered. I followed him. He was badly beating up a servant.

To cut a long story short the very next day Ashiq was arrested. He told the police: "There was another person with me." So I was also arrested. My in-laws in Mahim immediately got to know about this episode. I became very upset at the thought of facing them. My bride would form an extremely poor opinion of me. She must be weeping at the very idea of having had the knot tied to a scoundrel from whom no escape was now possible.

I put myself in the position of my bride for quite some time and very sincerely considered the options available to her. I finally decided to say very straight forwardly to aunty that after this incident, which was really very embarrassing, if she did not think it proper to send her daughter away with me, then I would be ready to divorce her. But when I expressed these thoughts to her, she turned around and said to me: "You must be mad if you think this way. We are convinced of your innocence."

I felt as if a weight had lifted off my chest but the superstition that my 'NIKAH' was unlucky for me increased. The condition of the company had further deteriorated and once again, instead of a salary only advances were being paid there against. The money in respect of my story was still owed to me. But it did not appear to me that I shall ever receive it.

My mother, on the insistence of my in-laws, meanwhile had fixed the date for the formal send-off of the bride. It was now nearly a year since the 'NIKAH' had taken place. Those people had probably sickened of the waiting but I was in no great hurry. In fact one could say that my heart desired that the send-off should not happen. I was anxious because I knew that I could not run a household and a decent girl, for the rest of her life without any fault of hers, would have to spend it in total misery. But the day had been fixed and for me this was no less than hell breaking loose.

The condition of the weekly "MUSSAWAR" had improved tremendously. Its office had been shifted to a better location. There was a telephone available. Mr. Nazir now had a small car in which he used to move around hither and thither obtaining advertisements.

The two of us now lived in that office. I used to go to Mahim every Sunday, where occasionally I would catch a glimpse of my wife through the open doors, and after taking dinner in the evening returned to my abode. But before going off to sleep I still cursed myself for having played the game of marriage in which I was bound to be hopeless. However, there was nothing that could be done now. A situation akin to damned if I do and damned if I do not.

Only ten days were left to the send-off date when I suddenly woke up from slumber. I went out and in the same building as the office rented a flat for rupees thirty five a month. Mr. Nazir paid me forty, so I told him to pay the monthly rent. Now I had rupees five left over in which to feed myself and my wife!

I cleaned up the flat vigorously washed the tiled floor and the doors of the flat, which were utterly filthy, with caustic soda. Having completed the task and a faint hope in my heart, I went to see Nano Bhai Desai and to ask him for the arrears of my salary and the price of my story.

The Seth after hearing me out told me in no uncertain terms that he was not going to pay me even a paisa and a half. When I heard this terse reply, I was infuriated and started abusing the Seth. The result of the outburst was that I was thrown out. I immediately telephoned Babu Rao Patel (Editor Film India). I gave him the complete details and said that if Nano Bhai did not settle my dues I would go on a hunger strike and that this was my final decision. Babu Rao was well aware of my obdurate nature. He was disturbed. He rang up Nano Bhai forthwith and said to him that if Manto were to start a hunger strike the entire publishing media would support him. It was therefore essential to arrive at a settlement.

No decision was arrived at on the telephone but when Babu Rao met with Nano Bhai later in his office I too was summoned. Nano Bhai apologized to me and it was finally mutually agreed that I accept half the amount due in settlement of my claim. A post-dated cheque for rupees nine hundred was given to me. A few days later when the due date arrived I rang up Nano Bhai that the date had arrived and I was going to cash the cheque he requested me to meet him first.

When I met him he in a heart broken tone said to me that there was no money in the bank. He asked if it would not be possible to agree to rupees five hundred in cash. I immediately agreed although my hard earned due earnings amounted to rupees eighteen hundred out of which I was first given nine hundred and now five hundred. But I had no choice except to accept as only four days were left in the send-off date.

I took the company car, which had just enough petrol to get us to a petrol station where I had some put in it from my own pocket, and ordered the driver to go straight to the market. I had rupees five hundred in my pocket. I bought a few saris and other things for my bride. When I reached home my pocket was nearly empty. The flat, of course was absolutely bare with not even a broken chair in it.

There was an elderly gentleman that I knew. Hakeem Mohammed Abu Talib Ashq Azeemabadi was an extremely interesting but excitable person. When I mentioned to him that I was bringing a bride but the flat was empty, he took me to a furniture shop whose owner he knew very well. I was allowed to buy some furniture on easy installments. For instance, two steel spring beds, a cupboard for crockery and other things, a dressing table (though second hand), a writing desk, a chair and some other stuff.

When I started arranging the furniture in the flat I was quite disappointed as the two rooms were huge. The furniture had just disappeared in it. So I purchased two small stools and put them in a corner but they too were swallowed up like the other furniture by the vastness of the rooms. Whatever I could find from wherever was placed in the rooms and I started to dupe myself into believing that the flat now looked filled up.

Doomsday finally arrived. In the morning I sat in the office of "MUSSAWAR." My mother had come over to the flat. I had told her that I was going away to arrange the bridal party to take along to the bride's house. Mr. Nazir had sent invitations to various people most of whom worked in the film industry. In other words my bridal party was one like out of a film. Mian Kardar, Director Ganjali, the famous actors E. Billimoria, D. Billimoria, Noor Mohammed Charlie, as well as Mirza Musharaff, Babu Rao Patel and the heroine of the first colour movie Padma Devi participated.

When Babu Rao Patel came to know that there was only my mother in my home, who alone would have to entertain the invitees, he sent Padma Devi over to assist my mother.

I had arranged for chairs on hire and from the Irani restaurant bottles of Vimto. The expense on these could be easily paid for by myself, therefore I was least worried on this account. I was of course extremely worried and deep in thought about how to run the household?

I had just taken my seat in the office when my sister from Mahim called and enquired after me. I replied, ala Agha Hashir: "The lion is in the cage." I told her that I was at that time overcome by yet another dilemma. Preparations for the bridal party were underway, but there were only Annas four and a half in my pocket. A pack of cigarettes would cost four annas and matches two paisas and that will be that! She was not in a position to help me. Her husband had not given her permission to join the send-off ceremony and to see her brother dressed up as a bridegroom. Still, she said to me: "May God bless you. Just stop your car in front of my house for a few seconds. I want to see you." I did not talk to her further as she was getting very emotional. Putting the telephone down I went to the neighbouring barber shop and hamam for a hair cut and a bath. All this was achieved on pay later terms.

By the evening I had smoked the entire pack of cigarettes. In my pocket there was now only a half full box of matches.

I changed clothes donning the suit presented by the in laws and knotted the tie in place. When I looked at my reflection in the mirror I looked like a cartoon, so had a good laugh.

Before the lights came on all invitees had assembled. Padma Devi and my mother entertained everyone. Finally, this party started moving towards Mahim in a cavalcade of ten, fifteen cars.

I was seated in Nano Bhai's car. There was no head gear or sehra. The hair length was decent. When we were nearing Jaffar House I asked the driver to take the car further down the road. There on the footpath stood my sister. Her eyes were full of tears. As soon as she had finished tousling my hair lovingly, blessed and congratulated me, I hastily returned to the car and asked the driver to reverse it.

Aunty had arranged a feast on the open terrace on the top floor of the building which was very nice. Rafiq Ghaznavi, Director Nanda and Agha Khalish Kashmiri engaged in a most interesting chit chat. Everyone ate well because the food was tasty and very well prepared besides being exactly in the Kashmiri tradition. After the meal a general conversation started. Agha Khalish Sahib recited a humourous verse which was put together impromptu by him. When this ended I was summoned downstairs and the bride entrusted to me.

I thought all of this was a dream. Various thoughts were racing through my mind and the bride was with me. I held her by her hand and in a tremulous voice said: "Let us depart."

We went downstairs. Billimoria offered his car. My mother was with me. She first seated the bride, then herself and finally asked me to come and sit next to her. She was between my bride and me. On the lap was the Holy Koran sheathed in velvet and my bride's and my necks heavily garlanded. When the motor started mother started mumbling a holy verse. I was egging to tease the bride but my mother was in between us and reciting the Koran. My naughty desire iced over immediately.

I do not know how and in what time the distance was covered. We were suddenly home. It was an old building constructed more with wood than brick. It was known to have been a grand hotel of Bombay once upon a time won in a wager from a friend by His Highness the Aga Khan.

My mother took the bride upstairs to the flat. I stayed back to thank my friends. In the meantime Mirza Musharaff arrived in the truck containing the bride's dowry. Dining Table, a bed with springs, side tables, a sofa set, chests etc. etc.

When the truck had been unloaded, Mirza Musharaff and the truck driver started arguing about the rental to be paid. This went on for sometime during the course of which Mirza Sahib gave a full display of his clownish behavior. Finally, when the argument was over, all the stuff was taken to the flat and temporarily placed here and there. Mirza Musharaff whilst departing whispered in my ears: "Boy, look here! Do not let us down!"I was dog tired. My throat was as dry as wood. Therefore I could not respond to the clown Mirza.

The next day I felt that a quarter of my body had turned into a husband. I was very satisfied with this feeling. I thought I had started seeing a tight rope strung across the balcony and imagining nappies hanging on it for drying!

A FEW MONTHS IN AMRITSAR

Bari Alig

In Lyallpur (now Faisalabad) whenever I used to pass the clinic of Hakeem Nooruddin Sahib, he would invite me in, seat me next to him and start an intellectual discourse. I, in utter respect of him, would listen to him and occasionally make an inconsequential contribution. I was one of those young friends of Hakeem Sahib who were impressed by his speeches and had started taking interest in political issues. In the early days of 1932 during one of our meetings he said to me: "Ghazi Sahib is going to start a daily newspaper "MUSAWAT" from Amritsar. He has asked for you so that you may work there in the newspaper."

I replied: "Sir! I have very little experience in journalism. What will I go and do there?"

"Your articles are regularly published in newspapers" he responded.

"Sir, there is a vast difference in writing articles and composing a newspaper. I do not wish that Ghazi Sahib may be displeased with my work," I replied.

"A good writer of articles with a little effort can turn into a good journalist. Go get ready. Give my warmest regards to Ghazi Sahib."

Having said his bit he became busy in some other work. I took my leave of him. In the next two to four days I decided on going to Amritsar. I had never been there before but the Jallianwala Bagh tragedy had created some sympathetic feelings in me for Amritsar.

In those days the bus fare compared to rail fare was much less. So I undertook the 125 mile journey by bus. On reaching Lahore, one had to change the bus for the onward journey to Amritsar. Most of the passengers in the bus from Lahore were from Amritsar. It became apparent from their style of conversation that they were fully aware of the Amritsari traditions and practices of its past. Because I belonged to a city which had nothing to do with old traditions, therefore every bit of the Amritsari chatter enhanced my interest in that city. There were a few other passengers from Peshawar, Kabul and Bokhara who talked about the samovar in such a manner as if Amritsar was a city of the Middle East.

The bus stopped at the terminal. I hired a tonga and proceeded towards the wide and clean avenue known as Hall Bazaar. As soon as we entered the road a large signboard with "MUSAWAT" written across it was seen hanging on a building. I entered the office and Ghazi Sahib welcomed me with affection and warmth. A few hours later I had started work. Several days later Atta Mohammed Chishti (later known as Haji Laq Laq) also joined the editorial staff.

Chishti Sahib, appearance wise, looked like a French intellectual. He had lived for a long time in the Middle East and had only recently returned to the Punjab. He was quite conversant with English, Arabic and Persian languages. He usually wore a silk suit. He had brought with him a large number of Arabic magazines. After looking at them I was impressed by the standard of Arabic journalism. Chishti Sahib did not like the local newspapers very much. His biggest problem, to begin with, was that he was quite unaware of the politics of this region, but as soon as he came to understand the local state of affairs he started expressing opinions on its high standard.

Once he pointed at a copy writer and said to me: "Munshi Sahib has just asked the peon to get half a packet of cigarettes for him. Does this sort of thing also regularly happen here?" I replied: "Of course! You may ask for one cigarette only should you so desire." He heard this and kept quiet but the expressions on his face were clearly asking "What kind of a country is this?"

Chishti Sahib had hardly been there for six or seven days when Ghazi Sahib informed me that since his cook had disappeared therefore Chishti Sahib and I would have to eat out for the next few days. I said to him: "No problem. But please tell me where the bazaar is?" " You do not even know this?" "No sir." "You have been here for three weeks and you still do not know where the bazaar is? Right outside is Hall Bazaar. Have you not been there?" "No sir, ever since I got here I have not been downstairs except the first day when I saw a few shops from the tonga that I came in." Ghazi Sahib turned and walked away to his room leaving his final words ringing in our ears: "God's curse! You have turned this newspaper office into a shrine."

I took Chishti Sahib along with me and together we walked into Hall Bazaar. We were looking at the shops on both sides of the street till Chishti Sahib spotted a billboard and said: "Shiraz Hotel." We hesitantly entered the restaurant and found some young people sitting at two or three tables. We were more interested in the food, but still bits of conversation that the young men were having floated into our ears. Chishti Sahib wanted to say something to them but on hearing my advice that: "Travelers should not interfere in the affairs of the locals," he agreed to stay quiet.

We got up to leave the restaurant as awkwardly as we had entered it. Chishti Sahib went ahead while I stopped at the counter and said to the Manager: "Sir, both of us work in the "MUSAWAT." If we sometime order tea etc. please do send it to us." On hearing my request the pleasant young person introduced himself: "My name is Aziz." "Aziz Shirazi, I presume?" The Manager said: "No sir, this servant of yours is known as Aziz Ahmed Amritsari. And what is your good name?" I told him our names and took leave of him.

Later in the evening we again went to "Shiraz" for dinner. After the food when we were sipping lemon tea, "Qehwa," Aziz Sahib came to our table, enquired after us and started introducing the young gentlemen sitting at a table near us: "This is Mr. Saadat Hassan Manto. This, the famous photographer Ashiq and that is the Amritsari litterateur Mr. Salees."

In those days Akhtar Shirani had become very popular and Aziz Sahib was an ardent admirer of his. He wanted us to have a meeting with Akhtar Shirani, but neither one of us knew this renowned poet of the time. So we kept on listening to the conversation of our new found friends who seem to know Akhtar

Shirani personally. Soon the theme of this discussion changed from romanticism to politics. Whilst this was going on another gentleman arrived and was thus greeted: "Welcome Vakeel (Lawyer) Sahib." During the course of discussion the topic now focused on death sentences. The lawyer gave a legal rundown on the matter. Saadat Hassan requested me for my point of view. I spoke for a few minutes referring to a speech of Victor Hugo which had been translated and printed in "ALHILAL" (Calcutta) and a book of his entitled "The Last Day of a Condemned Man." Saadat said: "I have this book. Would you like to read it again?"

The next day, with the said book under his arm, Saadat arrived in my office. I took the book from him. Right in front of Saadat sat a few copy writers in a line. Above each of the scribes hung an electric bulb and all were busy writing on pieces of yellow coloured paper. The young man was taken in by this sight and after obtaining my permission ventured closer to where they were seated. He would look at times at the yellow paper, then hold a steel penholder in his hands and intently gaze at it and then eye the scribes and myself. Five or ten minutes later, Saadat Sahib came over to me. He wanted to have a chit chat but since the time for Copy was at hand, I pushed a couple of magazines toward him and excused myself for about fifteen minutes. Though the magazines did not seem to interest him he kept turning their pages. During this time I started putting the copy together at my table. He threw the magazine aside and became engrossed in watching me do the layout for the newspaper. When it was done, we started conversing. Neither one of us could bear the burden of a formal conversation. However, in this meeting we had come near each other. We had become friends.

Two or three days later Saadat again came to my office. It so happened that a press invitation from a local cinema to a film premiere was lying on my table. As soon as he saw it he enquired of me as to when I would go to see the film. As I was not interested in the film and wanted to send someone else, I with some effort got Saadat to agree to go to the premiere only on the condition that he would write a few words about it for the paper. The next day "MUSAWAT" carried the few lines from our film correspondent which made my friend look extremely happy.

This incident took place sixteen years ago. But I am sure the publication of those few lines roused the short story writer hidden inside my friend Saadat.

I had, by now, become well acquainted with the geography of Amritsar. North to south, Amritsar district ran for approximately sixty miles. From East to West its width was probably five to seven miles or less. This district was spread in the northern part of the Bari-Doab from East to West and looked like a leveled terrain. But the ground actually rose towards the River Beas. Near River Ravi the water table was to be found at about fifty two feet of depth. Amritsar's nearness to a mountain range, plenty of forests, abundant cultivation, the presence of rivers and canals all helped to make its weather temperate even in the months of May and September. I was able to clearly feel the difference in the weather of Lahore and Amritsar during the summer months. The early days of May in Amritsar were generally better than the middle April weather of Lahore.

No traces of any ancient city can be found at the present location of Amritsar. But in this district there is a village called "SANGLA." When Alexander the Great crossed the Ravi he had to face tremendous resistance from the ruler of "SANGLA." There is a small town between Lyallpur and Sheikhupura with the same name which vies for this honour. But when you look at the trajectory of Alexander's military route and his crossing of the River Ravi, there can be little doubt that SANGLA village, district Amritsar, is deserving of the honour of the encounter between the army of Alexander and the SANGLA ruler.

During this time I had also become acquainted with Abu Saeed Qureshi and Hassan Abbas. Both were very good friends of Saadat. All four of us used to go to Ram Bagh (Garden) for an evening stroll. This garden is located in the North West corner of Amritsar Civil Lines. At this precise location the Sardar's of the "Bhangi" tribe had constructed a mud fort which was razed in 1819 by Maharaja Ranjit Singh and a garden ordered to be laid out in its place. When the garden was ready two years later the Maharajah named it Ram Bagh. The traces of a fortification wall around the garden can still be seen. To save the garden from attackers two huge gates supported by massive pillars were erected. Atop the inner gate, constructed in red stone, is a "Bara Dari". There are several other structures still standing that had been constructed under the Maharajah's order. Expert craftsmen from Delhi had been summoned by Faqir Azizuddin. Ram Bagh is certainly a beautiful garden and an excellent place for recreation. This lovely garden and "THANDI KHOI" (Cold Well) were separated by only the width of a road. Those who came to the gardens did not go back without drinking the chilly water of the "THANDI KHOI." Neighbouring the well were sweetmeat shops that were famous for "POORIS," dumplings and of course sweets. Each one of us had adopted the practice of settling the account with the shop owner at Annas eight or ten after having had dumplings worth Rupees one and half or two. Some other persons also joined this gang of recreational walkers.

One night whilst we sat in the garden it was unanimously agreed that a free thinker's forum should be launched. The bye laws and rules of this forum were an excellent representation of inexperience and immaturity. For instance:

1. At least two members of the forum will walk through Hall Bazaar daily in the afternoon.

2. They shall not converse with each other on the way. They may talk to non-members.

3. It was compulsory for each member to wear in summer flannel trousers and Khaki shirt.

4. Must have a meal per day in the Bazaar.

5. Will have a haircut only four times a year.

6. Will not drink "LASSI" (butter milk).

7. Will make a fool of a non-member at least once a month.

One evening neither one of us had enough money to pay for the other's food. In order to overcome this financial emergency the four of us decided to pool our resources. The total funds collected amounted to less than Annas six. As we walked down the Railway Bridge we saw a person who had laid out a piece of cloth to sit on and was selling "DAL and ROTI." One of us went forward to give him the order but the man was taken somewhat aback. But as soon as we all sat on the piece of cloth he became happy. Hassan Abbas, Abu Saeed Qureshi, Saadat Hassan and I had a meal for Annas four and a half. After buying two betel leaves and two cigarettes we still had one paisa left over which was pocketed as a token of remembrance of the day. However, the paisa did not stay there for long because when we heard a heart wrenching wail of a blind beggar and the paisa was given to him.

We the members of the Free Thinker's Forum were sitting together one evening after having completed our quota of making fools. Saadat appeared a little depressed on this account as he had yet to accomplish this task, when Ashiq, the photographer, arrived. "Please come, please come, Artiste Sahib" said Saadat greeting Ashiq. Saadat, it was clear to all, had decided on some naughtiness and he conveyed this intent to us through gestures which were suitably responded to. Saadat started talking of the weather and said: "It goes to Lahore's credit that the traffic police there now wear jackets made of ice." "Utter nonsense," retorted Ashiq. Saadat, however, in a very purposeful and decided manner replied: "This is nothing to trifle about. This is the age of Science. If electricity can run fans then why should it be so difficult for jackets to be made out of ice?" Ashiq went into deep thought, so the topic of the conversation was changed. A few minutes later we all dispersed.

The next day in the evening while the four of us were seated at SHIRAZ, Saadat started insisting that he had achieved in making a fool of Ashiq. The rest of us opined that Ashiq's silence only indicated a semi-achievement. We were still on the subject of making fools when Ashiq entered the restaurant and in

a flash of lightening picked up a large ladle and whacked it across
Saadat's head. Saadat responded with a tea cup. They were now
grappling with one another and fisticuffs were hurled. Finally
when both were bleeding from the nose and mouth we intervened
and pulled them apart. "What is the matter Ashiq Sahib? Please
tell us what has happened." "You think I am mad," he stopped
and added "I have just returned from Lahore and no traffic cop is
wearing an ice coat there. Am I mad?" Someone immediately
said: "No! Not at all! You are very intelligent. It is Saadat who is
mad when he talks such nonsense." "I shall not leave him. I will
teach him such a lesson that he will remember his entire life," said
Ashiq and raised a fist at Saadat. Few minutes later the two
opponents made up and together departed for the same doctor to
get their wounds bandaged.

At this time leftist thought had started entering politics.
After the failure of some movements started by young men, a few
people expressed the desire that politics should be kept aloof
from polarized emotional issues. But the leadership required to
create this atmosphere was nowhere to be seen. Some politicos
tried to fill up this gap. They according to their views tried to
bring a scientific angle into politics and even set up a party called
the Anti Imperialist League. I too was invited to a meeting of this
party which used to be held in a dark room located on the
western end of Jallianwala Bagh. This was the same place where
on April 13, 1919, on General Dyer's orders the assembled
gathering, which had congregated to protest the arrest of Doctors
Saifuddin Kitchlew and Satya Pal, was fired upon. The total
number of participants in the League meeting were no more than
eight or ten. I could barely understand twenty percent of the
analysis of the current political scenario that was presented at the

meeting. But for the first time I understood the influence of International state of affairs on local conditions. After being done with the meeting I met Akhtar Shirani (deceased) for the first time.

A lot of admirers of Akhtar Shirani were waiting for him at SHIRAZ. Shirani Sahib asked me to accompany him. We talked whilst walking to SHIRAZ. Akhtar Shirani spoke at length on the linguistic issue. He elucidated on the effect of Pushto grammar on Urdu language. The brightness in his eyes and the innocence on his face were adding to his personality. This was the time when the poetry of Akhtar Shirani was being much talked about and thousands of people were impressed by his character. I was one of those admirers.

Free Thinkers forum was in disarray. Serious thought and talk tried to replace the tomfoolery and naughtiness. We all had also turned somewhat sober. Saadat had in this while translated Victor Hugo's book. On his insistence I read the manuscript end to end. It was a good translation. A few months later this translation was published by Urdu Book Stall, Lahore. The extent of the success of his first effort can be measured by the fact that he was appointed to work for "HUMAYUN" by Hamid Ali Khan Sahib. Saadat continued to translate Russian short stories for another three to four years. Saadat's sudden transformation into a writer created awe, envy and worry amongst most of his circle of acquaintances whilst only two of his friends were extremely happy at this new found skill. And they were Abu Saeed Qureshi and Hassan Abbas. Saadat Hassan Manto's new literary activity and the publication of his translations of the

short stories in "HUMAYUN" encouraged these two
gentlemen to write. So, the three of them jointly translated an
Oscar Wilde drama entitled "VERA," (THE NIHILISTS),
into Urdu. As far as I can remember the translation of "Vera"
was published by a bookseller of Amritsar. The write up for
the publicity of this book that I penned, was printed in huge
posters by the publisher and pasted on the walls of every street
and lane of Amritsar. The public at large could not be over
awed by these posters for long as the very next day the police
had them taken down. I and Saadat started tailing the person
who was taking the posters down and in the process reached
Darbar Sahib (The Golden Temple). Both of us went inside to
have a look at the building. In the City and District of
Amritsar there are very few archaeological sites. Fateh Abad,
Norang Abad and Serai Amanat Khan do have traces of some
caravan Serais. In Amritsar the Khairuddin Masjid is very
beautiful but it was constructed not too far back in time.

The "MUSAWAT" closed down. I went over to stay at
Saadat's home. Saadat's very large house was located in "Kucha
Wakeelan." A room towards the rear of the house was organized
for us to carry on our reading and writing work. Abu Saeed
Qureshi and Khwaja Hassan Abbas also sat in this room and
wrote their short stories. I too wrote the first few pages of my
first book "The French Revolution" in that room. The doors of
this room remained wide open twenty four hours a day. There
was no restriction on any one coming in or going out of the room
except that they should not disturb others who were at work
there. After having lived in this place for several weeks I returned
to Lyallpur in September 1933.

There are only sixteen years between 1933 and 1950 but during this time the distance between Lyallpur and Amritsar has increased far too much.

WHY DO I WRITE SHORT STORIES

Honourable Ladies and Gentlemen!

I have been asked to explain why I write short stories. I do not understand the 'Why'? The meaning of why in the dictionary is for what reason or purpose and how.

Now what can I tell you about why I write a short story. It is somewhat puzzling if I kept the 'how' in mind and answered that I sit on a sofa in my room, take a paper and pen in hand and start writing a short story after saying "Bismillah" (in God's name). My three daughters constantly make a rumpus. I talk to them, as well as decide on their differences of opinion. I prepare a salad for myself. If someone comes to meet me I also entertain them but keep writing the short story.

If you were to ask me 'for what reason or purpose' do I write then the answer is: first, I write a short story because I am addicted to this form of writing just like alcohol; if I do not write a story I feel as if I have not worn my clothes or I have not had a bath or I have not had a drink.

The fact is that I do not write a short story rather the short story writes me. I am not a very educated person even though I have penned over twenty books. I am at times amazed by the thought as to who is this person who has written these excellent stories which become a subject of court cases on a virtually daily basis.

When the pen is not in my hand then I am simply Saadat Hassan, who knows not Urdu, nor Persian, English or French.

I do not carry a story in my head but in my pocket. I am not aware of this and I keep pressurizing my brain to produce a story. I also try a lot to act as a story writer. I smoke cigarette after cigarette, but no story emerges from my head. Frustrated, I lay myself down like a barren woman. I am disturbed by the fact that I have taken cash advances for stories that still remain unwritten. I toss and turn. I get up and feed my pet birds. I push the swing for my daughters. I sweep the house. I pick up the numerous pairs of small bootees that are littered all over and put them neatly in one place. But the damn story that lies lodged in my pocket does not move to my brain. I writhe in anger. When the frustration deepens I go to the bathroom but even that does not help.

I had heard that all great men think their best thoughts in a bathroom. But my experience has taught me that I am not a great man as I cannot even think in a bathroom. But it is amazing that I am still considered to be the biggest short story writer of Hindustan and Pakistan.

I can only say that either my critics are under a delusion or I am taking them for a ride or bewitching them. But do excuse me as I started talking of bathrooms. The fact is that I can swear to God that I have no knowledge as to why I write short stories or how I write them.

Most often what happens is that when I am totally riled, my wife tells me to stop thinking, just pick up a pen and start writing. I on her insistence pick up a pen or pencil and start writing. The head is totally empty, but the pocket is full and a short story automatically emerges.

Viewed from this perspective I do not consider myself to be a short story writer but a pickpocket who picks his own pocket and hands it over to you. Where will you find a bigger idiot than me?

INDEPENDENCE DAY

When Hindustan was divided into two parts I was in Bombay. One heard the speeches of Quaid-e-Azam and Pandit Nehru on the radio. Once partition was effectuated I was a witness to the turmoil that took over Bombay. Earlier one used to read in the daily newspapers, reports of Hindu-Muslim rioting. At times five Hindus were killed and sometimes   five Muslims. On the average the scale of killing and bloodletting remained more or less even.

In this connection I will narrate an incident. My newspaper delivery boy would regularly toss the daily "Times of India" through the kitchen window. One day – a day of rioting – someone suddenly knocked on the door at the usual time that the paper arrived. I was taken aback and went to find out who was knocking. I saw a stranger standing at the door with that day's newspaper in hand, so I asked him: "Where is the newspaper delivery man who comes here every day?" The stranger replied: "Sahib, he is dead. Yesterday in KAMAI PUR someone stabbed him with a knife. But before dying he told me to deliver the paper to such and such person and also get the dues from him."

What went through my heart at the time cannot be described. A day later, on the road, adjacent to my house, called Claire Road, in close proximity of the petrol pump I saw the dead body of a Hindu ice seller. His ice trolley was standing near his carcass and the slabs of ice were dripping cold water directly upon his blood. The blood had frozen and now resembled a mass of jelly.

Those were strange days. There were riots upon riots and from their womb two countries took birth, a Free Hindustan and a Free Pakistan. It was a scene of immense helter-skelter. Hundreds of well to do Muslims were boarding airplanes to fly to Karachi to witness the celebrations of the birth of a new Islamic Republic, while thousands more, cringing in fear, were hiding lest some great disaster strike them.

August 14 arrived and Bombay, generally known as the "City of Brides," was decked up as a gorgeous, brand new bride. It was a flood of lights which swept through the city of Bombay on the night of August 14, colourful, small, gay lights. I think, so much electricity had probably never been used up by this city in its entire life.

B.E.S.T. (Bombay Electric Supply Corporation) had arranged for a tram car especially for this occasion which was lit up with coloured electric bulbs on all four sides. These were arranged in such manner as to resemble buntings of the tricolored Congress flag. The tram car moved through the city all night.

The bigger buildings were all lit up. The English shops had made special arrangements. The decoration of White ways and the House of Frasers was to be most appreciated.

Now let us observe the scene in BHINDI BAZAAR. This is a famous street of Bombay which in the local dialect is called the area of "Mian Bhais," in other words Muslims. There are a lot of hotels and restaurants in this street. Some are called "BISMILLAH" (In the name of Allah), and some "SUBHAN

ALLAH" (Allah is Great), and more or less the entire holy book had been used here. However, no restaurant or hotel was called "NA AAUZ BILLAH" (God Forsaken). This street is Bombay's Pakistan. Hindus were celebrating their Hindustan's Independence and Muslims that of their Pakistan. I was awe struck and wondering what was going on. In BHINDI BAZAAR shops owned by Hindus were flying the tricolor banner and everywhere else the green Islamic flag of the Muslim League fluttered.

In the morning when I went to BHINDI BAZAAR I witnessed an amazing scene. The entire bazaar was wrapped up in green buntings. Outside one restaurant a huge painting of Quaid-e-Azam, obviously done by a novice, was displayed in shocking bright colours and two electric fans were directed towards it. Anyway I will never forget the sight as Muslims were extremely happy that they had achieved their Pakistan. But where was this Pakistan? What is it? No one had the faintest idea. They were only overjoyed as it was only after a long time that they finally had an occasion to celebrate.

In the Rampuri Dada Restaurants many a cup of tea were being drunk and PASSING SHOW cigarettes lit up to celebrate the making of Pakistan. Betel leaves with betel nuts from KALA KANDI and SANKI were being consumed in large quantities staining the fingers of all novices with betel nut juice and limestone paste.

I was amazed by what was going on but the most astounding fact was that on August 14 no one was murdered in Bombay. People were busy in celebrating Independence. What was this Independence? Why was it achieved? What changes would this Independence bring to their lives? No one gave a thought to these matters. On one side slogans of "PAKISTAN ZINDABAD" resonated while on the other side that of "HINDUSTAN ZINDABAD."

Now I will share some amusing incidents relating to Pakistan, which is our new born Islamic Republic. Last year on Independence Day a gentleman was trying to take home a dead, dry tree which he had chopped off. I said to him: "What are you doing? You have no right to cut this tree down." He responded: "This is Pakistan. This is our property." I kept silent.

The locality that I lived in, before the partition had taken place, was once a beautiful place. The square which was covered with heavy layers of grass was now totally bald. During the evenings naked young children used to play in the square. One of my daughters lost a large ball that she used to play with. I thought it would probably be somewhere in the house. But on the fourth day I saw some children playing with it. When I enquired from them they responded: "This is our ball. We bought it for Rupee one and Annas four." The fact was that the ball was priced Rupees four and Annas fifteen. Since in Pakistan you would not dare quarrel with anyone therefore I refrained from doing so and left my daughter's ball with them as if it was their right.

I would like to narrate another incident. A person was busy uprooting the brick tiles from the floor just outside my house. I said to him: "Brother, please do not do this. This is an outrage." He responded: "This is Pakistan. Who are you to stop me from doing this?" I did not react and remained quiet.

I took a radio to be repaired to a radio repair shop. I forgot about it until a month later when I recalled that I had to revisit the repair shop. So, I went to the shop and was told: "You did not come back for some time. Therefore I have sold your radio and adjusted the proceeds against my dues for repairing it."

Last year a day before Independence Day I received a notice saying that as I was not considered important enough a person therefore I should provide sufficient cause as to why I should not be ejected from the house that was currently occupied by me. If I were in fact an unimportant person then the government perhaps had the privilege that it should catch me just like a plague ridden rat and eliminate me. Fortunately, I have remained unscathed so far.

Finally, I would like to share another amusing incident with you. After the creation of Pakistan when I reached Karachi I found it to be in complete disarray. I thought that I should immediately leave for Lahore. So, I went to the Railway Station and asked the Booking Clerk to give me a first class ticket to Lahore. He replied: "You cannot get this ticket as all seats are reserved." I was used to the Bombay environment where everything was available on the black market. So I said to him: "Please charge me some more." He, in a serious tone, responded: "This is Pakistan. I used to indulge in this practice previously, but now I cannot do this. All seats are reserved. You cannot get a seat at any price."

And I did not get the ticket at any price.

FOREWORD

The first edition of this book was published in Bombay. After Partition the complete manuscript was handed over to 'Kutb' Publishers Limited before going over to Pakistan. From there I wrote to Ali Sardar Jaffrey who was in those days working for 'Kutb' that the only way to expedite the publication of the book was for him to pen the foreword to it. I wrote that whatever he chose to write would be acceptable to me. He wrote back:

"I will very happily write the foreword to your book although there is generally, for this book, no need of a foreword and particularly a foreword written by me. You know that there is a lot of disparity between your and my literary perspectives. Despite this I hold you in respect and have great expectations from you."

On receiving the letter I wrote back to Jaffrey Sahib: "Fine! Let the book go forth without a foreword." But during this time I received another letter from him which informed me that he had after all written a brief foreword and included it in the book. This foreword is part of the first edition of the book entitled "Buffoon." I removed it from the second edition of the book not because, God forbid, I had formed a poor opinion of Jaffrey Sahib or started disliking him. Actually, a few days back the so-called Progressive Writers of Bombay had created an inane rumpus about my writings and by a stroke of pen 'ex-communicated' me from the realms of literature. In view thereof I did not consider it proper that a very active member of this forum should remain attached to a "reactionary" like me.

When a short story from this book, "BABU GOPI NATH," was published in "Adab-e-Lateef" I was still residing in Bombay. All Progressives lauded it. It was declared the best short story of that year. Ali Sardar Jaffrey, Ismat Chughtai and Krishan Chander in particular were extremely appreciative of it. Krishan gave it a prominent place in "BAAL KA SAYE." But then God knows what happened that all the Progressives turned against the greatness of this short story. In the beginning it was subjected to some discreet criticism. A whisper campaign of referring to it as distasteful was started. Now all the Progressives of Hindustan and Pakistan have started calling this story reactionary, immodest, provocative and atrocious.

Exactly the same treatment was meted out to another short story of mine "MY NAME IS RADHA," although, when it was first published, writers of all hues had eulogized it. Ali Sardar, after he had penned the foreword titled it "Towards Progressiveness" for the book "BUFFOON," and wrote a letter to me: "I would like to know your opinion about the foreword. I wrote it with great love and admiration. I intend to write a rather longish article on your short story writing. To date you have only been abused by decadents. To expect anything different from them is only a waste of time."

On reading these lines does not one feel like slapping all of these words of his on the faces of the Progressives and thus permitting reactionaries to snigger quietly. In the same letter Ali

Sardar Jaffrey had written: "Your story "KHOL DO" is considered by me to be a masterpiece of this era."

The tragedy for the Progressives or with this story was that it was published by monthly "NAQOOSH," Lahore, then under the editorial ship of the Guru of Pakistani Progressives, Ahmed Nadeem Qasmi. Else, this story too would have been externed from the realms of literature and I would have been left gaping at the red faces of the Progressives.

My book "Black Borders" was disliked by the Progressives only because the foreword had been written by Hassan Askari, whose name had already been blacklisted by them. So, Ali Sardar, again, with lot of love and admiration, wrote to me:

"I have received news from Lahore, that Hassan Askari is writing a detailed introduction to your new book. I fail to understand the connection between you and Hassan Askari. I do not consider Hassan Askari to be sincere at all. The information gathering network and arrangements thereof of the Progressives are well established. The news from here reaches the 'Kremlin' through the grapevine very, very quickly." The news that Ali Sardar had received there from was, indeed, well founded.

The result therefore was that even before "Black Borders" was subjected to print it had been black listed and condemned to the retrogressive trash bin.

The wonder is that when Ali Sardar Jaffrey lifted his pen to write the foreword to "BUFFOON" he never appeared to have thought of the connection between Manto and him. After all he did say that there was a difference in both our literary perspectives. But my Progressive friends do not indulge in thinking. This, perhaps, amounts to "Negativism" for them.

I shall now present you with an outstanding illustration of not thinking. The magazine "SAVERA" of "NAYA ADARA," whose editor is Malik Nazir Ahmed Chaudhary, is a "Representative of Modern Progressive Literature Movement." In it, on the one hand, by including my name in the black list I am condemned as a reactionary, opportunist, individualistic, dreamer and lover of good things, whilst on the other "NAYA ADARA" is advertising a new story of mine in the following words:

"Saadat Hassan Manto is an epitome of honesty. He in his hand holds the double edged sword of truthfulness which he uses mercilessly in the dense jungles of Government and Society thus slashing the veils of hypocrisy. He is abused, but he smiles. Without any consideration of prayer and punishment he steadfastly moves ahead on a path on which only he can move."

When I read this advertisement in the "SAVERA" instead of smiling I had burst out laughing. Forget the "Many will be benefitted by reading this" tone of the advertisement and think if whether these Progressives and their publishers, regardless of their respective consciences, are not trudging on a road which they alone can only walk. A few days back Ismat Shahid Lateef (Chughtai) at the Bhopal Conference had, in front of a packed gathering, in an overtly masculine manner denounced all those short stories written by her which did not conform to the scales of progressiveness. Why don't these progressive publishers take a cue from the honest approach of Ismat? They must burn to ashes all those works that have been black listed and classified as reactionary. Were they to do this I would willingly kiss their hands.

In the end I would just like to say that I have nothing against Progressiveness but am extremely annoyed by the incomprehensible somersaults of the so-called progressives.

INNER FEELINGS

Today I feel like talking to you, the readers, of my writings, without the usual formality of forewords and introductions. Although in most of my short stories, dramas and articles there are matters that have a direct connection to that part of my heart and mind which is generally reserved for one's own self, but since it is over powered by the various facets of a story therefore you see it in a personalized form.

Today my heart is very sad. A strange depressing feeling engulfs it. Four or four and a half years back when I said good bye to my second home, Bombay, the place where I had spent the most industrious part of my life, my heart was similarly sad. That piece of land had adopted me, a person who was a drifter and spurned by his own household, in its fold. That city taught me that I could live happily on two paisas per day as well as rupees ten thousand per day. If one desired to live as a depressed individual in either situation one could do so. One could, in this place, do what ever and howsoever one wanted. No one here indulged in fault finding or sought reformists. Every difficult task had to be undertaken by oneself. Every important decision of one's life had to be taken on ones own. Whether one lived on the footpath or in a grand palace, it was of no concern to anyone. Whether one went or stayed, one did not feel any different. I am where I am and shall remain so. I stayed there for twelve years and learnt all that I could and it is only due to this that I find myself present in Pakistan now. If I move from here to somewhere else I shall be present there too. I am a walking, talking representation of Bombay. Wherever I live, my own world shall also live.

I was depressed after leaving Bombay. My friends, whose friendship I was proud of, were there,. I was married there. My first child was born there. The second one also saw the first day of its life there. It was in that place that I had earned and spent a few thousand and hundreds of thousands of rupees. I loved it then and I love it today!

I, for a long time, rebelled against and still rebel against the upheaval that had resulted from the division of the country. But later I accepted this horrendous reality in such a way so as not to allow depression to come anywhere near me.

I dove into the sea of blood that had flowed from the veins of humans as a result of the inhuman act of other humans. I picked out a few pearls of essential humanity from the laborious efforts of humans draining the last drop of blood from their fellow beings. These were tears of annoyance that came out of the eyes of some humans as a result their inability to put an end to their inhumanity. These pearls I presented in my book "SAYAH HASHIYA" (BLACK BORDERS).

I am a human, the same human who rapes humanity, who turns destruction into glory, who exhibits and sells like all other meat, the flesh of humans. I am the same human who achieved the status of God's messenger and I am the same human who tainted his own hands with the blood of messengers. I possess the same weaknesses and qualities that other humans have. Believe me, I was extremely saddened when some of my contemporaries ridiculed this effort of mine; they called me nonsensical, a jokester, a mattoid and a reactionary. A dear friend of mine even went to the extent of saying that I had a habit of taking out of the pockets of human carcasses unburnt cigarettes, rings and other things and making a collection of them. This dear friend of mine also had an open letter addressed to me published when he could have quite conveniently handed it over to me. In it too he had openly showered only ridicule on "SAYAH HASHIYA."

Being a human I became extremely angry. In that state, I, in response to this slime, prepared something equally filthy that would have stuck to the faces of these critics of mine forever. But then I thought and felt that committing this act would be a blunder. There is no doubt that an eye for an eye is human nature but to remain silent is a reflection of being intelligent, patient and tolerant.

I was angered not because 'A' had perhaps understood me wrongly but because 'A' had, in current style, at the slightest wink of a foreign elaborate and serious movement, toed its line, doubted my intentions and measured me on that gauge where "redness" alone was deemed gold.

I was annoyed at what had happened to these people. What kind of progressives were they as they were headed towards destruction? What kind of red was this which was galloping towards blackness? What was this labour friendliness which instigated a labourer to demand wages even before doing a stroke of work? What kind of a challenge was this to the capital of their labour? Perhaps they themselves desired to be armed with capital and are therefore ready to give away their beloved weapons of hammer and sickle into the hands of the rivals. What was that subtle reasoning in their literature which caused a poem to be presented as a machine and vice versa?

I was annoyed by their daily manifestos, their lengthy resolutions, their different statements spiced directly by the Russian Kremlin and transported via the farmyards of Bombay to reach McLeod Road. Such and such Russian poet had penned something, such and such Russian writer had made that statement and such and such Russian intellectual had made an observation. I am angered. Why do we people not talk only of the region where we live and breathe? Have we stopped producing intellectuals? If yes, then is the only treatment left for this state of infertility, the dissemination of 'red' thought!

Since I was angry nobody listened to me. After Partition there was a total state of chaos and confusion in the country. People were engaged in getting houses and mills allotted to them as well as running after high and influential posts. Nobody had the time of the day to think that after such a massive upheaval conditions could not remain the same as before. The old paths could have turned into broad avenues or obliterated forever. No one could say anything about this with certainty. What would be the difference between a Government of foreigners and our own? Nothing definite again could be said. What might be the atmosphere like and how may thoughts and feelings be properly formed in it? What kind of relationship might exist between the State, Government, the individual and the Party? These were matters that required deep thought and discussion. These were such issues where foreign prescriptions were not required to be acted upon. But alas! Our intellectuals yearning for leadership acted in great haste and jumped into the deep end where rudderless they lay rotting.

The Progressive guardian angels of literature had already decided that no member of their party shall work for an official paper or write in it. I opposed this decision of theirs and tried to make them understand that this was not only totally wrong but also ridiculous, because it reflected lack of confidence that the party of Progressive Writers had in the steadfastness of its members. Furthermore, such a decision should have been taken by the opposition. But I would have declared that absurd as well because any ruler would only select what is agreeable to it.

Our rulers too indulged in this absurdity but later and only after the Progressives had beaten their own drums of their own lack of confidence. Radio Broadcasts and pages of government newspapers and magazines were now no longer available for the expression of Progressive thoughts. Later some Progressives were jailed under the all encompassing Law and Order Act. Government is a second name for absurdity. I do not desire to comment on the innumerable absurdities committed to silence the Progressives.

I am sorry that Ahmed Nadeem Qasmi, Zaheer Kashmiri and others of similar ilk who are very decent individuals and whose mind and body cannot in any way be linked to conspiracy hatching have needlessly been jailed. One is interested in making 'brothers' and the other 'sisters.' One does not know how and where the Government saw political naughtiness in the undertones of these simple habits of theirs.

Without rhyme or reason and in a state of total anger the Government has jailed these people. They had probably been handed over to a barber who would distort their appearance. After some time when they come back on being released who knows what kind of humans they may have turned into. Will they be shaven from head to toe or will they be covered in hair? Will they be acclaimed as heroes or martyred leaders or forced to sell local medicinal concoctions on the footpath? Perhaps they will have repented from writing poetry and short stories or they might tread thereupon like a strait-jacketed person. There is no element of ridicule here because if I too were to be stuffed in prison I would say exactly the same thing for myself. Maybe I would say a little more than this, as I am an extremely sensitive person.

The Government and the Progressive Writers Party both became victims of inferiority complex. I was sorry about it then and I am sorry about it now. I was saddened more in respect of the Progressives who needlessly became entangled in politics. These chemists were preparing a potion of literature and politics based on the prescription suggested by the Kremlin. The patient for whom the mixture was being prepared was never asked what his pulse rate or his condition was. No one bothered about it. The result, as is before us, is a state of limbo in literature.

My heart is very sad today because all those magazines that represented the Progressive writers have had to, along with their demigods, take unexplained somersaults. At the end they had to scratch off all the advice, statements and resolutions from paper. In order to again secure the cooperation of those writers who had been blacklisted and condemned forever by them, they had to offer all kinds of excuses and regrets.

I feel very sad today when I see those who had refused to cooperate with the Government in reviewing their decisions. Why did they not think that in the very large domain of man's struggles the most important effort is the one of feeding the stomach.

Man's efforts may enable him to reach the moon or the intensity of his madness may enslave Gabriel, but the fact is that for the sake of his stomach one may at times have to even indulge in praise of an idiotic Nawab. This is a great tragedy of mankind but such tragedy is the other name of man.

All the anger in my heart had now transformed into sadness. I was now sorrowful and down-hearted. Whatever I had seen and what I was witnessing increased the sorrow. My current existence is full of problems. Labouring day and night I am only able to earn enough to eke out a living. This troublesome feeling is eating me like termites from within. If I were to drop dead who would look after my wife and three young daughters? I may be a writer of profanity, a desperate loony, jokester and reactionary but I remain the husband of a wife and the father of three girls. I am shudder at the thought that if any one of them fell sick and for their proper treatment I were forced to beg at every door. There are friends of mine who are in a greater state of destitution than me and if I cannot help them in a timely manner then this pains me a lot. In worldly affairs if I see my own or someone else's head hanging down then, by God, the sight saddens me too much. But when I think that if after my death the doors of radio and libraries were opened for my writings and my short stories given the same status as the verses of the late Iqbal then my spirit would become extremely restless. In view of this restlessness I am most satisfied with the treatment so far meted out to me. May God save my desiccated bones in my grave from the termites that may want to destroy them.

I am very sad today when I hear that those around me, who have had a hand on the pulse of literature, speak of inertia in literature, on its decline and suspended state. This kind of talk is quite similar to the absurd talk of Islam being in danger. Literature is tied to the existence of life in the same way as Islam, as a power, can never be a subject of regression. It can never be subject to dilatoriness or stagnation. The power of atom was present before its discovery and will remain so even thereafter. The wrong use of it or its non usage does not mean that its power has diminished or is about to die.

Literature is alive with the same force and brilliance as before. There is no question of dilatoriness or stagnation enveloping it. It is our own inertia which is attributed to literature. The causes of this state should not be looked for in literature but in our own minds. This is not a difficult task. If we move hither thither from the deictic path of literature then we should not say that the route has been removed.

Politics is a different domain. To indulge in it through usage of literature is not correct. In the same way as to reach the real goal of literature it would be a mistake to take the convoluted route of politics. No matter how much drum beating takes place to propagate the literature of Soviet Union but it is a fact that the hypocritical writings emerging from there, printed on hundreds of thousands of sheets of paper, are not literature but something else. An example of this can be excerpted from the latest writings of the Russian writers.

No one ever had or will have any kind of monopoly on literature. This is not the kind of work that may be contracted out. "Literature is engulfed by inertia" is an absurd pretense. Those who talk of "Islam in danger" are the very same who a few months back were shouting from various minarets that the Progressive writers have sustained the exalted status of literature even after the partition of India. They said it was dying but kept alive by the progressives who gave their blood to it. It is therefore amazing that as soon as a few of their members were arrested, existence of literature was once again endangered!

I feel very sorry today. Once I was accepted as a Progressive but later I was classed as a reactionary, and now once again they, who ordain, are getting ready to acclaim me as a Progressive. They believe that I am a Progressive, in other words a communist, a red. At times in anger, they accuse me, from time to time, of penning obscenity and want to prosecute me. On the other hand the same authority releases advertisements in the official publications stating: Saadat Hassan Manto is the most well known and best litterateur and short story writer of our country whose pen never stopped writing even in the days of the recent turmoil. My saddened heart trembles at the thought of this fickle minded government showing its pleasure with me and pinning a medal to my coffin. This would be the biggest insult for my greatest love!

After Partition I have presented the following books in the shown order to you. You can very well judge my mental state from them:

1. Harsh, Sour and Sweet ("TALKH, TURSH AUR SHIREEN")

2. Taste of Stone ("LAZZAT-A- SUNG")

3. Black Borders ("SAYYAH HASHYA")

4. Empty Bottles, Empty Boxes ("KHALI BOTTLAIN, KHALI DABBA")

5. Cold Meat ("THANDA GHOSHT")

6. The Godliness of Nimrod ("NAMROD KI KHUDAI")

7. End of Monarchy ("BADSHAHAT KA KHATMA")

I now present to you this latest collection. In it only two of the short stories, namely, "YAZID" and "1919 KI AIK BAAT" have been published earlier whilst all others are unpublished. How long did it take me to compile this anthology and how long did it take to be printed and presented before you, may be easily determined from the relevant dates. The last short story "MUMMY" in the anthology was started on October 16, but when the news of the assassination of the Prime Minister of Pakistan, Khan Liaquat Ali Khan, reached me my mind totally blanked out. Thereafter my second daughter was afflicted by tuberculosis. So I remained very unsettled for very many days. As a result the collection was inordinately delayed.

October 28, 1951

THE SHORT STORY WRITER AND
SEXUAL ISSUES

No matter how insignificant a thing may be it could be the cause of a big problem. If a mosquito somehow gets through a mosquito net, the problem of throwing it out, killing it and taking measures to stop other mosquitoes from entering the net are created. But the biggest issue, the mother of all issues, was created when Adam felt hungry. And a lesser but most amusing one was created when the first man in this world met the first woman of this world.

Both these issues, as you know, relate to two different kinds of hunger but which are closely related. These two hungers are the reason behind all the economic, religious, social and political and war related issues that we witness today. If the bloodied veil is lifted from the current war we shall see behind it mounds of dead bodies, a hunger for territory and nothing more.

Hunger, of whatever kind, is very dangerous. Those hungry for freedom when confronted with chains of slavery will resort to revolution. Those hungry for food, if not fed, will eventually try and snatch someone else's food. If man is denied the sight of a woman then he might look for the image in his fellowmen or animals.

Of all the adversities that exist in this world hunger is their mother. Hunger teaches begging, it germinates criminal activity, it leads to the proffering of human body for a price and it causes extremism. The assault of hunger is very aggressive, its attack intense and its wound very deep. Hunger produces madmen, madness does not produce hunger.

No matter which nook of the world a writer may come from, no matter whether he is progressive or reactionary, old or young the issues of the world, strewed all over, remain within his eye span. He writes about them selectively, at times in favour and at times against.

The writer of today is not too different from the writer of five hundred or more years ago. The label of new and old is tagged on everything by time alone and not man. We are today referred to as modern writers. The tomorrow to come will regard us as dated and lock us up in cupboards. But this does not mean that we lived in futility or we needlessly emptied our heads. When the hands of a watch move away from the first digit to the second it does not mean that the first digit has been rendered useless. After travelling the full distance the hands of the watch return to the first digit. This is the principle of the clock and also that of the world.

The new issues of today are not basically different from the old issues of yesterday. The ills of today have resulted from the seeds sown in the past. The sexual issues confronting the modern writer were present in exactly the same way for the old writers. They wrote in their style and we today write in our style.

I cannot understand why I am questioned again and again on sexual issues. Perhaps it is so because some people refer to me as a progressive or perhaps because some of my short stories are about sexual problems. It may well be so because some people deem the modern writer "sexualized" and desire to excommunicate them from the realms of literature, religion and society with a single stroke of pen. Whatever the reason maybe, I present my point of view hereunder:

Food and stomach, woman and man – two very old, well established and eternal connections. What is more important, food or stomach? Is woman more needed than man? I cannot say anything about this because my stomach wants food but I do not know if the grain is as desirous of my stomach as my stomach is for it.

Still whenever I think about earth giving birth to stalks of corn I realize that it could not have been in vain and I feel elated that it is perhaps for our stomach that the fields are full of the swaying golden stems and maybe my stomach did in fact come into being first and the ears of corn later.

Whatever may be, but this fact is as evident as a clear day that the world of literature is closely related to the two aforementioned relationships. The devolved books, that is, literature of God, are also not lacking in reference to food, stomach, man and woman.

But the question arises that when these issues are so old that they are even mentioned in the devolved books, then why does the modern writer waste his time on them? Is it because the relationship between man and women is such that it must be repeatedly revisited, and according to some, only to spread obscenity? The answer to this question is that by advising only once not to thieve or lie, has the whole world stopped thieving or lying? If this were so, then perhaps only one messenger would have been required, but as you are aware the list of messengers is fairly long.

We, the writers, are no messengers. We present one thing, one issue in different situations and then examine it from various angles. Whatever we understand from this we put before the world and never force them to accept it.

We are neither lawyers nor censors. Accountability and legislation is some body else's work. We criticize Governments but are not the rulers. We prepare blueprints of structures but are not its builders. We inform of illness but are not in charge of the dispensaries.

We do not write on sex and those who do are in the wrong. In our stories we spotlight on the condition of particular men and particular women. If the heroine of our story is disliked by men only because she likes wearing white coloured clothes, then should other women not consider this to be a principle? Why did the dislike occur and under what conditions? The answer to these questions shall most certainly be found in our stories.

Those people who are looking for some new ways of titillation in our short stories will be disappointed. We are not teachers of moves. If we see somebody falling down in the wrestling ring, then we try to make you appreciate, according to our understanding, as to why the person fell.

We are optimists; we look for strains of daylight in the darkest of gloom. We do not look at any one in hate. When in the Red Light Area, a prostitute, standing or sitting on her balcony, spits on a pedestrian walking below, we unlike a lot of other onlookers neither laugh at the pedestrian nor abuse the prostitute. We stop in our tracks on witnessing this occurrence. Our eyes pierce through the semi-clad body of that woman belonging to a filthy profession and try to reach the depths of her heart. We will search therein, and, during the course of it, in our imagination, dissect that filthy and smelly prostitute, only to discover and present the real reason behind the incident and not just a photographic image of it.

Whenever a young, healthy and beautiful girl from a decent home elopes with a skinny, ugly and poverty stricken lad, we do not declare her accursed. Others may hang the past, present and future of the girl on the scaffold of superciliousness, but we will attempt to untie the very small knot which caused her behavior to become apathetic.

No two humans are very different from one another. The mistake that one man makes can also be committed by the other. When a woman can sell her body by setting up shop then all women of this world can do the same. But it is not the act of humans that is wrong but the conditions that envelop him and cause him to err and then reap the harvest of those mistakes.